tony's
Lactose Free
cookbook

The science of lactose intolerance and how to live without lactose

by **Professor Anthony K Campbell**
and **Dr Stephanie B Matthews**

For the first time – how to eat truly lactose free.

"Coming off lactose has given me my life back."

Published by Welston Press Ltd.
Registered in Wales No. 3887391

Welston Science Series No. 2

Copyright © Welston Press 2005

First Edition August 2005

Photographs Copyright © Steve McAllister 2005

Designed by SupaGrafix, Cardiff

Printed in Wales

Available from the British Library
ISSN 1474-6794
ISBN 0-9540866-1-9

The recipes in this book are original and not copied from any other source.
Any similarity to other recipes is entirely coincidental.

This book is dedicated to our beautiful children,

Georgina, Emma and Lewis.

Thank you for always making our family mealtimes very special.

contents

❖   ❖   ❖

figures and tables

❖   ❖   ❖

❖   ❖   ❖

❖　　　❖　　　❖

Professor Anthony Campbell MA PhD FLS FRSA

Anthony is an expert in the biochemistry of lactose intolerance and one of life's genuine enthusiasts. He is a true natural scientist who believes that science begins with curiosity, and that the challenge is to harness this curiosity, through our inventiveness, to discover how the living world works, and evolved. He also believes that invention is as scientifically challenging as discovery, playing a central role in the evolution of our culture and economy.

He has applied this philosophy to his own researches into what switches cells on and off in health and disease, and to developing platform technologies for clinical diagnosis and drug discovery, based on chemical reactions that produce light – chemi- and bio-luminescence*. He is also a passionate believer in Public Understanding of Science and Health, arguing that this is perhaps the issue of our time.

Anthony was born in 1945 in Bangor, North Wales, but grew up in London. He was educated at The City of London School, and obtained a first-class degree and PhD in Natural Sciences at Pembroke College, Cambridge. He is now Professor in Medical Biochemistry at the Wales College of Medicine, Cardiff University, and also has set up a science centre with a lab and seminar room for schools in Pembrokeshire. His researches have taken him from the biochemistry of deep-sea bioluminescence to the molecular basis of rheumatoid arthritis.

Anthony has pioneered an experimental strategy to study the chemistry of living cells, based on the genetic engineering of bioluminescent proteins. An international authority on intracellular signalling, and in chemi- and bio-luminescence, he has written three books in these fields, 'Intracellular Calcium: Its Universal Role as Regulator', 'Chemiluminescence: Principles and Applications in Biology and Medicine', and 'Rubicon: The Fifth Dimension of Biology'. He has more than 200 scientific articles, and several patents being exploited world wide. The chemiluminescence patents are now used in some 100 million clinical tests per year throughout the world. This technology received the Queen's Anniversary Prize for Higher Education in 1998. Anthony has wide experience in the Public Understanding of Science and Health, in Wales, nationally and internationally.

He founded The Darwin Centre for Biology and Medicine (Canolfan Bywydeg a Meddygaeth Darwin)** in 1994. The Darwin Centre aims to bring cutting edge science and entrepreneurship into everyday life, and to catalyse fresh inspiration in research, and in the presentation of science, through a University network linked to schools and the public throughout Wales, and a marine sabbatical centre. He has given many TV and radio interviews, and founded the Pembrokeshire Darwin Science Festival in 1999. This festival ran over 30 events from March-September 2000, involving several thousand participants, and is now in its 6th year. He has presented at several Public Understanding of Science and Health events, both nationally and internationally.

He was elected foreign member of the Royal Swedish Academy of Sciences, Uppsala, 2000, and, in 2002, founded AKRainbow Ltd, to exploit his bioluminescent protein technology.

He pursues an active life of research and science communication to schools and the general public, and was President of the South Wales Association for Science Education in 2002. In 2003 'How to Genetically Engineer a Rainbow' was exhibited at the Royal Society Summer Exhibition, where it was voted the best exhibit. The Pembrokeshire Darwin Science Festival in 2005 enjoyed its sixth year with glow-worm hunts, lectures, field trips and workshops.

He is married to Stephanie, and has five children.

*www.cardiff.ac.uk/medicine/medical_biochem/staff/campbell/index.htm **www.darwincentre.com

Dr Stephanie B Matthews MB BCh PhD FRCPath

Stephanie is an expert in the clinical management of lactose intolerance. She was born in Newport, Gwent, and grew up in Scunthorpe, where she went to grammar school. She then studied medicine at the Welsh National School of Medicine, in Cardiff, qualifying in 1978. She became a Consultant in Medical Biochemistry in the National Health Service in 1988, where she still works full time. Her speciality is Medical Biochemistry – the chemistry of how the body works. She runs special clinics for those with high blood cholesterol and food intolerances.

She has specialised in the study and treatment of people who have problems with blood fats, and is pioneering a treatment called LDL apheresis to reverse the furring up of arteries by cholesterol. This has extended into a professional and personal interest in nutrition, and scientifically-based healthly eating. The discovery of her own lactose intolerance has changed her life in more ways than one.

Stephanie believes in the need to communicate effectively with people in order to allow them to take ownership of their own health. She has tried hard to practice this in her own clinics for over ten years. She has mentored school children (10-18 years) in science projects with the Darwin Centre, of which she is a Director, and was President of the Association for Science Education for Wales in 2000. She became a Fellow of the Royal College of Pathology in 1998.

With Anthony, she has pioneered a science theatre project called 'Not the nine o'clock clinic' which has changed the way children with high cholesterol are managed. She was short listed for Hospital Doctor of the Year in 2003.

But Stephanie argues that her most important role is that of Mum to Georgie, Emma and Lewis, and partner to Anthony, a larger than life crazy scientist. She divides her time between home in Penarth, Pembrokeshire and Provence.

preface

This book could transform your life. The discoveries we have made in the past five years, and the recipes that have followed from them, have changed the life of our family in a wonderful way. As many of our 500 patients often tell us, "Coming off lactose has given me my life back". We aim to show you how you can find out whether you are suffering needlessly from intolerance to the sugar in milk – lactose.

We love our family suppers, and lunches at weekends! But it was not always so. We were fed up with grovelling at small tables in front of the telly. We wanted to enjoy our food with a nice glass of wine, and have a conversation, even a debate, with our family. But mealtimes didn't seem to be the welcoming event that we found in the family traditions of France or Italy. Six years ago we discovered that three members of our family were intolerant to lactose.

In fact, lactose in a whole range of dairy and non-dairy foods was quite simply ruining our lives. Intolerance to certain foods can cause a range of gut problems and symptoms all around the body, known as systemic symptoms. The possibility that these might be caused by lactose has been missed by the medical profession because it is not widely known that 'hidden' lactose is present in many foods and drinks often inadequately labelled, confusing a diagnosis based on dietary removal of dairy foods. Once we found this out, Tony changed all his menus, removing all milk and dairy products, as well as risk foods and drinks such as processed meats, patés and bread. We also stopped drinking beers and lagers. This cookbook, with over 100 mouth-watering recipes to enjoy, is the result. They will help you discover if you are being poisoned by the sugar in milk – lactose.

We have many people to thank. First, and most important of all, we thank all of our patients who have been so enthusiastic about our ideas and analysis. We thank the colleagues who have helped us uncover the science behind lactose intolerance. We thank particularly Jon Waud for all his dedicated lab work, his enthusiasm and new ideas, and Andrew Roberts for designing the DNA test. We thank also our colleagues Suzanne Watkins, John Green, and Jill Swift, and our colleague Ken Wann for his interest and enthusiasm. Also Dr Ken Mole for his enthusiastic correspondence about Charles Darwin's illness, and Jean Marie Bassot for the inspiration of Le Marteau where we found wonderful food cooked with ingredients fresh from the garden!

We thank particular friends like Howard Potter, unrelated to Harry Potter, but a wizard all the same at accounts, and in his typically unselfish way, at inspiring us to continue to develop original ideas when others were pouring cold water, or even boiling oil from the ramparts, on them. Our family, Georgina, Emma and Lewis, and David and Neil, have been terrifically supportive of this project. Their enthusiasm at mealtimes has been a great joy.

We will remember Thursday 19th August 2004 for a long time. As Georgina came out of her school with a look of amazement on her face, and small slip in her hand with 3 As on it, we were overjoyed. We knew she had achieved her dream of going to Oxford University. Without our discoveries, and the recipes in this book, it is doubtful whether she would have achieved this. We thank our mothers for their love, and for always showing such interest in our work. We thank particularly Stephanie's mother for being so helpful in looking after the children after school on so many occasions, enabling us to continue flat out with our work.

We thank also the Department of Medical Biochemistry and Immunology for financial support for our research programme.

Finally, we thank the people who helped to put this book together, Anthony's secretary Helen Cullen for her hard work on slide shows and figures, Steve McAllister for the terrific design and layout of the book – as well as the photos and diagram of the human body, and Tony and Anne Hallett of Windsor Bookshop, Penarth for their enthusiasm and for the distribution of the book.

Our researches have taken us from the patient bedside to a small pond in our garden in Pembrokeshire where Tony found a tiny invertebrate called a water flea that is helping us find how lactose causes all its bad effects on the human body. Our data highlight the wide range of systemic symptoms caused by lactose intolerance. These symptoms have important implications for the management of irritable bowel syndrome (IBS), and for doctors of many specialities including general practitioners. We now have a genetic test, with a new biochemical and clinical strategy, that provides a diagnosis within 48 hours in more than 75% of patients.

Yet still the only way to find out if you are intolerant to lactose is to remove **all** lactose from your diet for at least a month, and then monitor very carefully the effect this has on you.

We believe this is the first cookbook that has really got to grips with the problem of lactose intolerance and shows how you really **can** eat lactose free!

We hope you will enjoy preparing and eating the recipes we present to you here. Please let us know the results. We enjoy them every day.

À table! Bon appétit!

Tony and Stephanie

Every so often, a scientist like me stumbles on something rather odd, and then has to decide whether to ignore it or investigate it. This happened to me six years ago. Then I had no idea that this was going to completely transform my professional life as a biochemist, and my personal life as well. It is an extraordinary story with the result that - "coming off lactose gave me my family back".

An unusual case?

A few years ago Stephanie and I discovered a 53 year old woman whose life was being made miserable by severe irritable bowel syndrome (IBS), skin rashes, breathing problems, muscle and joint pain, diarrhoea, nausea and sickness and lack of concentration. She had had these since childhood. But they were now so severe that she was worried that she had Alzheimer's disease. Her doctor told her she had eczema, asthma and osteo-arthritis, and she was now awaiting a knee replacement operation. She was on a range of drugs, including skin creams, antihistamines, asthma inhalers, antibiotics, anti-diarrhoeals and strong pain relief. She was surprised when we decided to investigate her for lactose intolerance. This involved taking 50g of lactose orally, followed by an analysis of her breath for hydrogen gas. But this turned out to be negative. However she did record a range of symptoms in the gut and around the body (systemic) several hours after ingestion of the lactose. These included abdominal pain, nausea and vomiting, headache, light headedness, feeling drunk, heart palpitations, and joint and muscle pain. These remained severe for three days. So we advised her to remove all lactose from her diet for one month. This not only involved avoidance of food and drinks containing 'dairy' products, but also she was advised to avoid foods and drinks where lactose is present in large quantities without being on the label. Within one month she described her skin as 'wonderful'. Her asthma and sinusitis had gone, and her joints were much improved. She no longer needed any medication and was taken off the list for a knee replacement. An incredible story!

Our diagnosis of lactose intolerance has transformed her life. She has been well and off all medication now for over two years. Similar dramatic stories have been repeated among the 500 patients Stephanie and I have now diagnosed as having 'systemic' lactose intolerance. We now have a DNA test that provides a vital aid to diagnosis. Intolerance to certain foods can cause a range of problems in the gut and around the body. The possibility that these might be caused by lactose has been missed because the presence of 'hidden' lactose, added to many foods and drinks without being on the label, is not generally realised, confusing a diagnosis based on dietary removal of dairy foods. A major change in the clinical management of lactose intolerance and IBS is now required. And what is more, it is vital that there are recipe books like this one that enable people suffering from lactose intolerance to enjoy their meals.

Eureka!

Have you ever had a "Eureka!" moment in your life? Well I had one six years ago, and I want to share it with you. This is a truly remarkable detective story that turned personal disaster into a major medical quest for a completely new approach to understanding disease, and the quality of life we want to enjoy. It has exposed a food industry scandal that will reverberate throughout society, and will shock many, more so because the food manufacturers and supermarkets apparently seem oblivious of the problem.

Imagine the realisation that you are not going to be bedridden for the rest of your life, that you are not developing Alzheimer's disease after all, and that you are going to live to see your children grow up. Not only are you not going to die, but actually you feel fantastic! No wonder Stephanie and I look back on this as **the** eureka moment in our lives, a triumph for the lactose detectives.

Have you ever been labelled as a sufferer from migraine, irritable bowel syndrome or chronic fatigue? Do you suffer regularly from unexplained headaches and loss of concentration? Do your children complain of severe tiredness, or have bad eczema and hay fever, that all affect their performance at school? Or are you just one of those real problems that no one can work out? Have you been embarrassed to complain about your latest symptoms to your family or your doctor, because you know that they have already labelled you as a moaner and hypochondriac? A doctor may even have suggested that you see a psychiatrist! Do you have a friend who suffers from pain in the muscles and joints, often so bad that she finds it difficult to walk upstairs or to the shops? Or maybe you know someone who gets bad pains in the gut a couple of hours after a meal, and is even sick for hours or days on end. Well, if so, my eureka moment could be yours as well. Who would think that just one common ingredient in our food could cause all of these problems? Certainly not the people who have written the medical textbooks. Yet Stephanie and I have now studied very carefully, using established medical methods, several hundred people who have suffered from all of these problems, and who now feel fantastic. Their lives have been transformed by removing just one ingredient from their diet, lactose - to them the 'poison' in milk. Eureka!

Imagine a lady who couldn't walk upstairs, diagnosed with rheumatoid arthritis. Think of a boy who was hopeless at school, always complaining of tiredness and headaches. He was told to snap out it, and was referred to a child psychologist. Then there was the man who had seen every doctor you can think of for over 20 years, and yet was still plagued with a whole range of symptoms. And then there was the case of a doctor who herself was ill for days on end, and diagnosed as early menopause. It was cases like these, and we now have some 500, that are the reason I have written this book. The cause of all these people's illness was in fact lactose. Once Stephanie and I had diagnosed these patients correctly as lactose intolerant their lives were transformed. The lady diagnosed with rheumatoid arthritis can now run around the garden. The boy with so-called psychosomatic problems is now doing well at school. The man with symptoms for over 20 years improved remarkably. He had a daughter with eczema so bad she was often hospitalised. It disappeared when she too removed lactose from her diet. And once the doctor discovered that her problem was the sugar in milk, her hormones went back to normal. Then, at 44, she had the surprise of becoming pregnant! She now has a lovely 6 year old son.

Much of modern medicine rightly worries most about diseases that can kill you - heart attacks, strokes, cancer, MRSA, SARS, AIDS and so on. Medicine focuses on birth and death. But what about the middle bit? What about the quality of life we lead? Don't we all want to feel alert, energetic, excited both intellectually and sexually, and hungry not just for our next meal but for life itself?

Yes, of course, we all want to live to be a hundred. But if we feel awful all the time we can't enjoy ourselves, our family and friends, or our work. The story I have to tell, and that eureka moment, has already given several hundred people their lives back, when they had all but given up. No wonder they were depressed. I argue here that the problem Stephanie and I have uncovered may affect thousands of people, not only in our own country but also all over the world.

Many people try very hard to live healthy lifestyles. They make informed decisions about what they do and don't eat. Some decisions can lead to heated discussion, with arguments for and against different diets, such as veganism. But those who choose to follow this nutritional lifestyle are free to assess the evidence and make their own decisions. Some choices are lead by religious conviction. This book will cause disbelief and anger in some quarters. For example, orthodox Jews are not supposed to mix meat with milk. But has anyone told them that a product directly made from milk is added to meat products freely available in the supermarket? This book aims to expose this deceit, and demand that if lactose is added to a food or drink it must be on the label. At the time of writing this book, the Foods Standards Agency have failed to address this scandal. Let's hope some politician will read this book, and take action. I have been told that the regulations are about to change. We will see!

Stephanie's story

Stephanie had wanted to be a doctor for as long as she could remember. When she was just eight years old she had written about this dream in an essay entitled: 'What I want to do when I grow up', a story which remarkably has survived. In this little girl's story there was amazing insight, as she pondered the long training and hours that she would have to put in if she was to be a doctor. She also knew that she would have to pass lots of exams. Her creative alternative was to marry a millionaire instead! No one finds studying for exams easy, but for Stephanie there was an added problem. Why, for no apparent reason, was it sometimes effortless, and yet at other times it was arduous and impossible to concentrate or think straight. Everyone is like this you say. The severe hay fever affecting her every year from April to August did not help either, enforcing her to stay for long periods in sealed rooms where sneezing bouts lasted hours.

Emma's plea

"Daddy, Mummy isn't going to die is she," our lovely little Emma asked? She was just four years old when Stephanie was in the middle of one of her worst attacks. It was a heartrending moment that made me determined to sort out what really was wrong with her mum.

Stephanie was tremendously excited when the Medical School in Cardiff, the Welsh National School of Medicine as it then was, offered her a place. She needed just three Bs in her A levels - Zoology, Chemistry and Physics. She had worked hard for nearly two years since her O levels. The School were confidant that there was not going to be a problem in getting the grades required. But no one could predict the disaster that would jeopardise her chances, and destroy her dreams before her career had even begun.

Out of the blue, since she was a baby, Stephanie would get a violent attack of a blinding headache with nausea and vomiting. This had been labelled variously as migraine or bilious attacks. Stress was not a trendy diagnosis in those days thank goodness, or that would have been a favoured option for sure. Anyway her mother and grandmother had both suffered similar problems, so it was only to be expected wasn't it? These episodes could last just a day, but sometimes went on for several days at a time. And guess what? She had a bad one the day of her Physics A level. She flunked it. The first day of the A level exams was a 3-hour Physics theory paper in the morning, with a similar ordeal in the afternoon. Earlier that morning she had woken up with an attack. Hard as she tried she just couldn't concentrate. The attack lasted for two days, leaving Stephanie feeling very weak and washed out, affecting all her results.

She dreaded the day the results were due. When she finally plucked up courage to open the dreaded envelope her fears were tragically realised. Instead of the expected As in Zoology and Chemistry, she only got Bs. But worse still she only got a D in Physics, the exam she had sat on the worse day of the attack. There was no continual assessment in the 1970s, nor any chance to resit. The final exam was everything. What a disaster! Her dream was gone. Cardiff Medical School rejected her.

The problem was that if you feel 'ill', or not quite right a lot of the time, then the concept of normality is turned on its head. 'When did you last feel really well?' is a question many of our patients find impossible to answer. This was brought home when one of them, a four year old child, after dietary changes removing lactose from his diet, told his mother that his tummy felt funny because it didn't hurt any more. He had not complained before because the pain in his abdomen was his 'normal' state. No, Stephanie's condition was not normal, but nobody could help and the situation was accepted. The memory of sitting in that exam room being escorted every ten minutes or so to the toilets sends shivers up her spine even now. Naturally the standard of answers on that exam paper was dismal. Nightmare!

Fortunately this story had a happy ending, or I wouldn't be writing this book. Stephanie's school phoned up the Medical School in Cardiff. Luckily, she had carried out a research project on snails in the school pond. Also, there was the extra advanced paper known then as an S level for which she got a distinction. This, with the project, must have won the day with Cardiff. After two weeks of dejection, at 11 o'clock one Tuesday morning she got one of the most important phone calls of her life. The Welsh National School of Medicine were going to accept her after all! So Stephanie, after much elation, began as a medical student in October 1973. She did well, winning several prizes, and qualified fully as a doctor in the summer of 1978. But throughout her time as a medical student she still suffered from these episodes of sickness and headache, often with muscle and joint pain. And she continued to suffer from the bad hay fever she had had for as long as she could remember. None of the medical textbooks she read, nor the lectures or clinical studies she attended during her training, could pin down what was wrong with her. A typical range of explanations included - time of the month, chocolate, a hang over, or it must be some sort of bug or other. No one was really interested anyway. It was normal for her. I often wonder what might have been! Thank goodness our work described here has saved our own children from a similar potentially devastating fate.

'Come on get your self together', is a typical response from unsympathetic colleagues, or even family. Even if they don't say it, they often think it.

Then I met Stephanie, and she became my PhD student. Three years later her thesis was very well received by the external examiner. Stephanie became a doctor squared, and then passed the extra exams to become a member of the Royal College of Pathology, and thus a fully qualified medical biochemist, with a special interest in cholesterol, diet and heart disease. It will be little surprise to you that during this climax in her medical training we fell in love. I was at that time a senior lecturer in the same department of Medical Biochemistry, having been invited to Cardiff as a lecturer in 1970, after completing my degree in Natural Sciences and PhD in Cambridge.

I have a special interest in animals that make light - glow-worms, fireflies, luminous jelly fish, and the like. This may seem pretty weird for someone in a medical school, with the hope of finding the cause of rheumatoid arthritis. But in fact my curiosity about this wonderful phenomenon, called bioluminescence, has had a huge impact on medical research and clinical diagnosis. One of the inventions that I was developing with colleagues in the department when Stephanie arrived, is now used in some one hundred million clinical tests per year world-wide, and has brought in over £10 million in royalties to Cardiff University. Not bad on the back of a somewhat obscure luminous jellyfish. Then, in 1985, we married. A few months later Stephanie felt a weird taste in her mouth - a sort of metallic sensation. From her medical training she knew what this was! In fact she had been feeling sick for a few days. She was pregnant. In November 1985 we experienced the joy of the birth of our first daughter, Georgina. Yet this event was also a relief for Stephanie. She had had a pretty miserable eight months, feeling sick almost continuously, and with several of the symptoms she normally associated with her problem. This unpleasantness and drastic reduction of quality of life was to be repeated in the pregnancy that lead to the birth of Emma. But we all know that lots of women suffer from these sort of problems during pregnancy. You just have to put up with it. Or do you?

Stephanie was promoted to Consultant in Medical Biochemistry in 1988, the youngest such Consultant in the country at the time, to be followed by her election as a Fellow of the Royal College of Pathology in 1998. In the year 1991, I was promoted to Professor in Medical Biochemistry. At the time Stephanie was pioneering a fantastic treatment for heart disease, called LDL apheresis. This is like an oil change. You pass the patient's blood down a large tube. This removes the cholesterol. As a result the cholesterol-filled plaques in the arteries of the heart start to dissolve. Over a period of months the patients get better, and crucially live. It stops them having any more heart attacks. This is because her patients have all inherited the problem of a very high cholesterol. Sometimes this is three to four times that of the normal, healthy level. As a result her patients have had heart attacks in their twenties and thirties. Without Stephanie's treatment they would be dead. Yet this revolutionary treatment is still very poorly exploited in Britain. Wales has one of the worst incidences of heart attacks in the world. Stephanie's heart treatment centre is the only one of its type in Wales, and only one of five in the whole of the UK. Yet in Germany they have over one hundred. Even Italy has over sixty of these centres. And the USA is catching up fast. But Stephanie's patients were beginning to suffer from another problem. They were worried about her. During the 1990s her episodes of sickness and headache occurred more and more frequently,

5

wiping her out for days on end, and severely affecting her important clinical work. She had to cancel clinic after clinic. She began to consider what it could be. Medics know what the worst scenario can be. Did she have chronic fatigue syndrome? Was it early Alzheimer's? Stephanie started to worry that she had bowel cancer. Or was it simply stress? She was getting so desperate, as her problems got worse and the attacks came more frequently, that she seriously considered giving up work entirely, on the basis of ill health. And then she started to have other problems, of a more direct hormonal nature. So she decided to see a specialist in London.

'You have early menopause', he said.

'But can I get pregnant', Stephanie asked persistently. Another pregnancy was the last thing she wanted, with more sickness, a full time career, and two young children to look after?

'Absolutely not', the doctor answered. 'Your hormones have all shut down,' he continued in a voice that rang with apparent authority.

Famous last words! Stephanie returned to Cardiff, apprehensive but with hope. At least someone had found something wrong with her at last.

Then a month later, her curse struck again. She felt a severe headache coming on, and then the sickness started. She went on vomiting virtually continuously for three days. And another unusual symptom was a racing heart (tachycardia), particularly at night. Stephanie was very badly dehydrated, and had lost over a stone in weight in just a few days. Typically, as a medic, she refused to go into hospital! The children and I were getting increasingly worried.

It was then that Emma, in tears, asked me her heart-rending question. 'Is Mummy going to die Daddy?'

I thought, and thought and thought. I felt so frustrated. Surely as a biochemist of some international standing I ought to be able to solve this. I was determined to find the answer. But I had to wait for Stephanie to recover. Three days later, as she sat in the bedroom exhausted and drained, I joined her.

'We have got to get this sorted. We can't go on like this,' I said. I was passionate about most things, but this was beyond the pail. It had to be sorted, and fast. Our whole life, and that of the family, was being ruined. We were biochemists and medical experts. Surely we must be able to solve it? We needed to think like detectives.

'It must be something you did or ate the day before it started,' I suggested. 'What did you eat? Can you remember?'

Then that 'eureka' moment!

'Hold on. Do you remember that first night we spent together', I continued. 'I had to deliver my

Stephanie's original symptoms
Symptoms she had 'all the time'
- Daily headache (often waking with it)
- Intense fatigue would occur for no reason at any time
- Light headedness and loss of concentration making her unsafe to drive
- Muscle pain and heaviness
- Joint pain with severe stiffness, worst in the morning
- Racing heart (known medically as tachycardia), usually at night
- Severe hay fever in Spring and Summer
- Constipation

Main symptoms during an attack, usually lasting at least 3 days
- Severe headache (frontal)
- Continuous sick feeling (nausea) caused by a gut block (known medically as ileus)
- Vomiting, often every 30 minutes

first book to the publishers in Chichester, and we had taken the opportunity to spend our first romantic night together'.

'Remember at breakfast I was very surprised at your cornflakes?' I went on. 'You ate them without milk. Yuck! And I asked, are you lactose intolerant? You denied it vigorously! But the night before your latest attack I made a big cauliflower cheese, in a rich béchamel sauce with lots of milk, and the attack started the following evening. So what did you have for lunch that day?'

Stephanie thought for a minute, and then looked up. 'I finished off the cauliflower cheese, and I forced myself to drink a glass of milk. Even though I didn't like it, I thought it would be good for me', she replied.

'So, could it be lactose', I asked? I was more and more convinced that I was on to something.

'No it can't be. None of my symptoms are in the medical textbooks as being caused by lactose', Stephanie replied quietly.

She was still very weak, but starting to think clearly again. 'Lactose only causes gut problems - gut pain, tummy rumbling, gas, and of course diarrhoea,' she continued. 'I get the opposite. My gut stops. It's called ileus. But OK, to keep you happy I will do a lactose intolerance test on myself. I will have to take some lactose and measure my breath hydrogen for three hours. If it goes up I am lactose intolerant, if it doesn't then I am not. The hydrogen is produced by bacteria in the gut when they digest the lactose that isn't absorbed into the blood. This is why people with lactose intolerance produce a lot of gas'.

A week later, when Stephanie had, at last, got back to work. The telephone rang in my lab.

'I've got it', a quiet voice at the other end said simply. 'And I can feel a headache and nausea coming on. I'm going home.' But this time Stephanie felt elated, even though she knew she was about to be ill again. We had finally cracked it.

Eureka! It was lactose, the sugar in milk. And it was an intolerance, not an allergy to milk, that Stephanie was suffering from. Not only that, if we were right then we were going to rewrite the medical textbooks. This was certainly the most important personal discovery of my life. But I was also very excited that it might be the most significant original medical discovery of my career.

Within a week of cutting out all dairy products most of Stephanie's symptoms disappeared. She no longer had a daily headache, no longer had unexplained fatigue, and no longer had muscle pains, so bad that she could hardly walk. The constipation disappeared after a few weeks. She stopped having joint pains within a few months, and her hay fever didn't appear as usual that summer. In fact, she hasn't had to take an antihistamine since.

But this really was just the start of our story as lactose detectives. We began to find other people who had the same problem as Stephanie. But, just when we thought we had it cracked, it happened again. The family were in Greece. We had splashed out on a holiday in the North, a lovely beach and a hotel with three swimming pools. Just when we were relaxing with another lager at the beach bar, Stephanie said, 'I'm going to lie down.' And then another three days were wiped out as before.

'But it can't be. You have had no lactose,' I exclaimed exasperatedly.

Then the next year it happened again, in Italy this time. We must have missed something. It wasn't lactose after all!

Two holidays ruined. Then we made another major discovery. If you can't handle lactose it isn't good enough simply to avoid milk and dairy products. During the last forty years the food industry have been adding milk products, such as whey and lactose itself, to many foods and drinks. These include meat products, breads, cakes, and even lagers. And in most cases lactose is not noted on the label. Or if it is, then it is disguised as a milk product such as whey that many people do not realise contains lactose. It was the lager that hit Stephanie in Greece, and in Italy it was the mordatella, a very large sausage-like cold meat that we now know has milk in the ingredients. **Eureka!**

So those were my first two 'eureka' moments. First, realising that lactose causes a wide range of symptoms in tissues other than the gut not mentioned in the medical textbooks. Secondly, that there is a scandal in the food industry where lactose is added to a wide range of foods. Yet often this is not stated directly on the label. Then we had to ask ourselves whether any of our children had inherited the problem from Stephanie. Yes they had. Both Georgina and Emma needed to avoid milk and lactose. But this was an answer we came to in retrospect. We had in fact missed the fact that both our children had been suffering from symptoms and that, like Stephanie at her age, these were affecting their progress at school. Georgie was always complaining about pains in her knees. But she loved tennis, and we put it down to a sport's injury. These pains were so severe that she actually had X-rays and several consultations. She also, like Stephanie, had had episodes of headache with nausea and vomiting regularly since she was eight years old. But no one could explain either these or her joint pains.

Georgie's attacks seemed to occur every Monday, and almost caused a rift with some good friends. Every Monday Georgie was picked up from school with her best friend Laura by Laura's mum. Georgie always stayed for tea, but by 6pm she was usually throwing up. What was Laura's mum giving her?! At that time, just like Laura's family, our family diet was full of milk and cream, especially on Sunday with milk based sauces, home made trifles, and other treats. Georgie however, like most teenagers, always knew best. There was nothing wrong with her! But after much convincing she deliberately challenged herself with dairy products. Within 24 hours this was followed by symptoms. After coming off dairy products Georgie's pains and vomiting disappeared, and she started to perform much better academically at school, to the level we knew she was capable. At her primary school she had never realised her potential, but we never understood why. Now she has finished her A levels at the local comprehensive. She has taken off, literally, and she ended up one of the star pupils at the school. She had some marvellous University offers. All of this would not have happened if we had not helped Georgie remove lactose from her diet. We were thrilled when she got her 3 As at A level, and was accepted to read Engineering at Trinity College, Oxford. None of this would have been possible without my recipes, now available in this book.

So I embarked on converting all my cordon bleu recipes to lactose free, using soya milk and my imagination. My family moved on, and Stephanie and I continued our professional lives. Then . . . we found another case, a friend of ours, and then another, and another, all of whom were suffering similar symptoms to Stephanie. And no one could diagnose what was wrong, or treat them. We then realised that we had stumbled on the most important medical discovery of our lives, and one that we hope you will agree could completely change the direction of medical research and clinical practice in a whole range of diseases.

As lactose detectives, we needed to look afresh at diseases like rheumatoid arthritis, cancer, heart disease, multiple sclerosis and diabetes. Could our new-found mechanisms, revealed by lactose intolerance, be operating in these diseases too? After all many of the most common diseases have defied medical researchers, after decades of thousands of experiments and scientific publications, and millions of pounds of research grants.

It was when I realised the potential implications of our discovery, that I took a huge gamble. I dropped all my current research, and went to the library to find out all I could about lactose and bacteria in the gut. Now, some five years later, I have made the crucial breakthrough. As a biochemist, I needed to find the molecules that caused the symptoms suffered by the patients. I found a way to reveal them using a most amazing biological system. Not a human being, but a tiny invertebrate that I discovered through the Darwin public awareness of science initiative that I set up in Pembrokeshire, as it was used as a model system in schools. I found a tiny animal, in hundreds,

9

in our garden pond. I hope they may even revolutionise medical research. If you want to read more about this, then turn to '**The Science Bits**' that I have written at the end of this book.

Let me now go back to 1998, just after we had had that first eureka moment in Stephanie's story. As I have indicated already, it was then Stephanie and I started to find the same problem in lots of other people - colleagues at work, friends and acquaintances. We would meet someone at a party and start telling them our remarkable lactose detective story. By the end of the story, the face of the listener had changed dramatically.

'But that's me,' they would say. 'I get headaches all the time, and feel sick. And I get so tired. No one seems to understand. Can I come and see you tomorrow at the hospital?' And then Stephanie started to get referrals from colleagues. Often these were people whom the medical profession had all but given up on. Many had been labelled as irritable bowel syndrome (IBS), chronic fatigue syndrome (CFS), ME, and psychosomatic. There turned out to be so many of them that Stephanie had to set up a new clinic, the first food intolerance clinic in Wales. She now has a waiting list of over 12 months!! That's how widespread the lactose problem really is. But what should people with lactose intolerance eat?

What is lactose intolerance and how do I cope?
Lactose versus lactase

Lactose is the sugar in milk. It is made of two sugars 'stuck' together, galactose and glucose. So its scientific name is beta (ß) galactose 1,4 glucose. It is *the* sugar in the milk of all mammals, except in sea-lions and walruses who use fat instead. Lactose provides some 40% of the energy for a baby. Take care not to confuse 'lactose' with 'lactate'. Lactose and lactate are both derived from the Latin *lac* = milk. Lactate is in fact lactic acid formed from glucose, and is completely different chemically from lactose. When milk goes off in the fridge, the lactose has been converted by the bacteria to lactate. This is what happens when milk converts to cheese and yoghurt.

Since lact**o**se is a sugar it has to end in **-ose**. It is broken in two in the small intestine by an enzyme, lact**a**se, which in contrast ends in **-ase**, like all enzymes. All adult mammals, except white Northern Europeans (Caucasians) and some other ethnic groups (e.g. the Bedouins and African dairying tribes such as the Fulani), have a low lactase (**Table 1**). These people are called hypolactasic, hypo meaning low.

Lactose intolerance versus a milk allergy

You have lactose intolerance if you feel ill a few hours after eating or drinking lactose. An intolerance is not the same as an allergy.

Last Christmas a friend kindly gave us a box of chocolate brazils. I love them. But to Stephanie and Georgina, the reaction was Yuck! Milk chocolate! We can't touch that. On the back of the box there was however an amusing warning that provoked much laughter as we sat eating our Christmas pudding. There we read, 'This product may contain traces of nuts'. And this did not come out of a Christmas cracker! What this warning alluded to, of course, was not the Brazil nuts, but rather that the chocolate contained some nut extract, almost certainly from peanuts. People

Table 1. Different ethnic groups with low lactase and likely lactose intolerance.

Ethnic group (adult, unless stated)	% with low lactase and potential lactose intolerance
Chinese	>90%
Japanese	>90%
Indian and other Asian groups	>80%
Aboriginal Australian	>80%
Black African	>75%
American Red Indian	>70%
Eskimo	>70%
South American (total adults)	>50%
Mexican	>50%
West Indian	>50%
Spanish	>40%
Italian	>40%
Greek	>40%
Mid European (e.g. Hungarian and gypsy)	>40%
American (total adults)	30%
Finnish	20%
White Northern European	10%
White Australian	10%
Children under 2 years old (any ethnic group)	0-20%
Children between 2 and 10 years old	0-40%
Patients with IBS	>50%

Note: These numbers are very approximate, and intended only to give an indication of whether you are at risk. > means greater than.

who are allergic to peanuts come out in a rash, or worse still have major breathing problems, if they eat anything with peanuts or peanut extract in it. Similarly, some people are allergic to proteins that occur in milk. But an allergy is quite different from intolerance. Food allergies involve an immune reaction where antibodies, to proteins in the food to which the person is allergic, are generated. The symptoms are quite different from those of lactose intolerance. They are often very rapid, involving breathlessness and rashes. In contrast, intolerance is a biochemical problem as a result of something missing in body chemistry, in this case the enzyme lactase. If you have a low lactase you can't fully absorb the sugar in milk - lactose. When you don't digest it fully yourself, there are bacteria in the gut that will. As a result, the bacteria generate gases and toxins that then cause the symptoms of lactose intolerance.

Lactose intolerance and hypolactasia
It is important to distinguish between hypolactasia, a low level of lactase, and clinical lactose intolerance.

There are three causes of loss of lactase (hypolactasia):

- Complete loss of lactase at birth (congenital). This is very rare.
- Inherited loss on weaning. This is very common, the norm in all mammals, in fact.
- Secondary loss, as a result of ageing or intestinal damage, e.g. from infections such as rotavirus or the protozoa *Giardia*, or hormonal imbalance.

Only secondary loss is potentially reversible, and thus important to identify clinically.

The genetics of lactose intolerance are confusing, mainly due to biochemical individuality between and within different ethnic populations. Any infection of the small intestine is likely to lead to damage or loss of the cells there that contain the lactase, and thus cause lactose intolerance. This is why people and animals that have rotavirus infection or protozoa like *Giardia* have persistent diarrhoea. The lactase takes some time to recover after the infection has gone. This is why babies who get gastroenteritis are temporarily lactose intolerant after the infection.

Everyone has some lactase and so can digest some lactose. The question you must ask yourself is: what is my lactose threshold? Can I take say a couple of spoonfuls of cow's milk in a cup of tea? Can I even drink a glass of milk? Or am I so sensitive to lactose that I must be careful not to take any at all? Several studies have shown that patients considering themselves lactose intolerant can take 1-2 cups of milk (200ml = 10g lactose) during the day. Yoghurt, ice cream and cream can contain similar amounts to milk. The lactose content in many hard cheeses is quite low (less than 1g per dessert spoon, approx. 30g). You would have to eat a kilo (kg) of freshly-grated Parmesan to take as much lactose as there is in a glass of milk. Thus a spoonful of Parmesan on pasta is unlikely to result in symptoms. Butter contains only traces of lactose. Make clarified butter, as described further on, if you are worried. This is quite easy. The threshold for lactose varies amazingly between individuals. Where some can tolerate a glass of milk, others get symptoms with just a few grams of lactose from a chocolate bar. We recommend that you experiment carefully with various foods and drinks to discover your lactose threshold. Some people can, over months, adapt and increase their tolerance to milk. This occurs through the gut bacteria. Lactose can be reduced in dairy products by using an enzyme called ß-galactosidase, available in health food shops. This is sometimes labelled incorrectly as 'lactase'. Low-lactose milk is available in supermarkets made by this method. But it is quite sweet as it contains the galactose and glucose from the degraded lactose. Non-sweet low lactose milk has apparently appeared recently in the USA. The key to whether you get symptoms after taking lactose is the bacteria in your large intestine (see '**The Science Bits**').

Intolerance to milk was first described by the Greek philosopher, and father of modern medicine, Hippocrates (*circa* 450-370 BC) over two thousand years ago. But only in the past 50 years has the condition of lactose intolerance been fully recognised, and diagnosed medically. The medical textbooks tell us that lactose intolerance causes only gut symptoms: gut pain and distension, borborygmi (tummy rumbling), flatus (gas) and diarrhoea, and maybe nausea (feeling sick) (**Table 2A**). But we have found that lactose intolerance also causes vomiting, with many patients presenting with constipation due to reduced intestinal movement rather than diarrhoea.

And lactose also causes a range of symptoms around the body, called systemic, including headaches and light-headedness, loss of concentration, difficulty with short-term memory, severe tiredness, muscle and joint pain, runny nose and blocked sinus, itchy rash, asthma, heart arrhythmia, mouth ulcers, sore throat, and increased frequency of micturition (weeing) (**Table 2B**). These symptoms can begin just an hour or two after taking lactose, but can last 1-2 days or even longer. The right hand column in **Table 2** shows the proportion of people, diagnosed as lactose intolerant, with each symptom.

Many of our patients have simply been labelled 'unexplained irritable bowel syndrome (IBS)'. Unexplained, sometimes after all sorts of biochemical tests, and even endoscopy, colonoscopy and barium X-ray studies. Unexplained, because these people suffered not only from gut pain and discomfort, but also from symptoms around the body. The significance of these 'non-gut' symptoms had been missed because of the spasmodic nature of the symptoms. An individual can exhibit just 2-3 symptoms or the complete set, the prevalence varying from 20% to 100% (**Table 2B**). Also many people with irritable bowel syndrome (IBS) have other problems, in addition to lactose intolerance. Yet the lives of over 500 of our patients have been transformed by coming off lactose, after at last being diagnosed as lactose intolerant, often after years of discomfort and mis-diagnosis, including accusations of psychosomatic illness. Many were on all sorts of drugs, even ready for surgery having been mis-diagnosed as arthritic, or were to be referred to a psychiatrist. It's all in your mind they were told! If it isn't in the textbooks then it must be psychosomatic, the current medical dogma goes. Our data show that the textbooks have missed something very important.

'Hidden' lactose

The key problem, that is not well known, is the presence of 'hidden' lactose added to many foods and drinks and not directly on the label. This has to be one of the great food scandals. In the USA alone there has been a five-fold increase in lactose production in the last 10 years or so, reaching its present level of over 300 million kilos per annum. This lactose is added to animal and human food, a disaster if you are lactose intolerant. Lactose intolerance causes great distress in many patients, who often do not realise that this lactose is added to many foods and drinks, in addition to those directly from milk and other diary products, without stating this on the label. This is the big problem. The occurrence of this 'hidden' lactose is not widely known to clinicians or dieticians. This may explain the mysteries of many food intolerances which have been known for some time to cause many of the symptoms listed in **Table 2**. When the dairy exclusion diet apparently fails, lactose intolerance is often ruled out inappropriately.

The issue of 'hidden' lactose is a controversial one. Clear evidence for 'hidden' lactose is difficult to find in the scientific literature, many of the clues being either anecdotal or circumstantial. We are therefore urgently setting up a sophisticated system to measure accurately the amount of lactose found in a wide range of foods and drinks. Our evidence to date for 'hidden' lactose is as follows:

- There are many products on food labels that contain lactose without clear explanation (see **Tables 3 & 4**). Many of our patients have been caught out.
- High lactose concentrations have been measured in non-dairy foods and drinks.
- There are several peer reviewed nutritional papers published that state this.

- There are several web sites that highlight this problem.
- There are a number of books concerned with lactose intolerance that state this.
- Lactose production world-wide is huge (**Figure 1**). This lactose must be going somewhere.
- Several people who have worked in the food and drink industry have confirmed that they knew of lactose being added to certain products from their company.
- Bakers in some supermarkets, and some butchers, have confirmed that they know about the addition of lactose in breads or meat sauce powders.

Keep an eye on our web site for the results as we get them (**www.welstonpress.com**).

Table 2. Gut and systemic symptoms of people with lactose intolerance.

Symptoms of lactose intolerance	No. of people with symptom (% of total with lactose intolerance)
A. Gut related	
Abdominal pain	100%
Gut distension	100%
Borborygmi (tummy rumbling)	100%
Flatulence (gas)	100%
Diarrhoea	70%
Constipation	30%
Nausea	78%
Vomiting	78%
B. Systemic	
Headache and light-headedness	86%
Loss of concentration and poor short term memory	82%
Chronic severe tiredness	63%
Muscle pain	71%
Joint pain, and/or swelling and stiffness	71%
Allergies, such as:	40%
Eczema (skin rash)	
Pruritis (itchy skin)	
Rhinitis (runny nose)	
Sinusitis (stuffed up sinus)	
Asthma (wheezing and shortness of breath)	
Heart arrhythmia	24%
Mouth ulcers	30%
Increased frequency of micturition (weeing)	Less than 20%
Sore throat	Less than 20%

Note: Systemic = around the body.

The problem of lactose in food

As you walk around the supermarket it is really quite difficult to decide whether many foods contain lactose or not. I deal with the problem of deciphering food labels in the next section. So take care, they are often very unhelpful if you are lactose intolerant. And the supermarket staff may be poorly educated by their employer!

Our eldest daughter, Georgie, was in New York recently and went to a burger bar for lunch. She asked the man behind the counter whether the orange juice contained lactose. He answered unequivocally, 'yes'. Because some 30% of adults in the USA are hypolactasic, Americans tend to be more aware of the lactose problem. On returning home Georgie went to a similar burger bar and asked the same question. 'What's lactose?', was the reply from the man behind the counter. Quite disgraceful really!

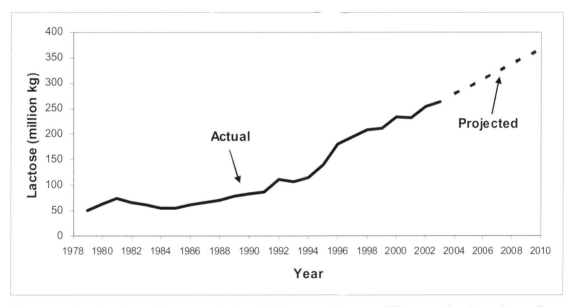

Figure 1. Production of lactose in the USA over the past 25 years (and projected).

In this recipe book I have chosen ingredients that should contain no lactose, except for a little cheese as mentioned. The **'Dos and Don'ts'** section aims to help you decide on food to choose and what to avoid. All milk contains lactose, from whatever source. So don't be fooled by people who tell you that goat's or ewe's milk is OK. It isn't, if you are lactose intolerant. Cow's milk contains nearly 50g lactose per litre, equivalent to about 3 tablespoons of pure lactose powder. Human milk contains even more, some 70g lactose per litre. We know the lactose content of many dairy products (**Table 3**). But what is very difficult to find out is the actual amount of lactose itself added to various foods, either directly or through a dairy product.

The recommendation of free milk to all school children needs to be questioned. If you are non-white Northern European, beware - your child will be hypolactasic and may get symptoms of lactose intolerance even from a glass of milk. Stephanie worked with one school which had a high

Somali population. The teachers were able easily to point out those children suffering with our syndrome. These children lacked concentration, were always very tired, and had recurrent headaches and gut problems. They were lactose intolerant, and should have been told to avoid milk.

But the problem is that avoiding milk and dairy products is not enough. As I have already mentioned, a large lactose industry has grown up during the last 30 years or so, adding it to many foods and drinks, often without telling the consumer on the label. So beware of 'hidden' lactose. Lactose has about one sixth of the sweetness of sucrose, the sugar you put on your cereal. Unlike sucrose or glucose, lactose cannot be metabolised effectively by yeast. So when added to juices or lagers lactose doesn't ferment. Thus lactose can be added to foods and drinks without causing a sickly taste, and without generating carbon dioxide or ethanol as a result of yeast metabolism. In the USA alone production of lactose in 1979 was about 50 million kg per annum (**Figure 1**). By 1999 this had raised five-fold. Now the estimated annual lactose production is approaching 300 million kg. This lactose is added to animal feeds and human foods and drinks.

Lactose is used as a browning agent in bread and cake mixes, and can be added as a 'filler' to processed meats, such as sausages and burgers. Reduced fat foods, such as certain mayonnaises and biscuits, can have added lactose. It is even injected into some chicken meat. It is also added to some soft drinks and lagers. Beware if your lager tastes sweet. Some breakfast drinks, powders and slimming products can contain more lactose then milk. We estimated the contents of one patient's weight reducing diet involved a daily intake of 100g lactose, equivalent to more than 2 litres of milk, yet it was not stated on the label! And lactose can be used in sauces supplied as powders to butchers and restaurants. This is why we have set up a method to measure lactose in food and drink so that we can advise our patients.

Lactose is also used as the most common bulking agent in pharmaceuticals. So take care! We calculated that a course of antibiotics meant that the patient would be taking over 5g of lactose a day, equivalent to 100ml of milk. Pharmacists are aware of this. You should ask them to give you lactose free drugs. Otherwise, as much as 50% or more of the tablet's weight can be lactose.

The lack of information regarding the lactose content of foods and drugs has major implications for the millions of people who are hypolactasic, and for ethnic groups, e.g. orthodox Jews who are forbidden to eat milk products with meat. Coming off lactose does not prevent you enjoying eating and drinking to the full, as I hope this recipe book shows.

Food labels
You need a PhD in Biochemistry to understand many food labels, they appear to be so complicated. And the lettering is often so small that you need a microscope to decipher it. So how can you tell from the label if there is any lactose added to a food you want to buy? Yes, sometimes buried in the list of ingredients you may find 'lactose'. Or the word 'dairy' may be on the label. But often the lactose is in something not so familiar, such as whey. Or it may simply be described as 'added sugar'. Don't be confused by lactate. As I have pointed out already 'lactate' is quite different from 'lactose', and fine if you are lactose intolerant. Lactose is often added to chocolate, even ones

Table 3. Lactose content of some foods and drinks.

Food or drink	Relative lactose content	Lactose as a % (*i.e.* g/100g or 100ml)
Dairy		
Lactose	Complete	100%
Whey	Very high	70%
Non-fat dry milk powder	Very high	50%
Cow's milk	High (47g/litre)	5%
Goat's milk	High (44g/litre)	4%
Reduced lactose milk	Low	1%
Lactose free milk	Very low	0-0.5%
Sour milk	High	4%
Buttermilk	High	4%
Commercial yoghurt	High	4%
True natural yoghurt	Moderate to low	2%
Cheese	Moderate	
Feta	Quite high	4%
Diet cottage	Quite high	3%
Parmesan (hard block for fresh grating)	Low to moderate	1%
Parmesan (grated in packet)	Can be quite high	3%
Cheddar	Trace to low	0-2%
Camembert	Not very high	0-1%
Edam	Low	0-1%
Some cheese products	Can be high	5-10%
Cream	Moderate	4%
Butter	Low	1%
Clarified butter	Very low	Should be 0
Chocolate	High	?
Milk proteins (casein, *etc.*)	Low, but can be present	0-2%
Non-dairy		
Processed meats *e.g.* sausages and salamis	Added, can be high	?
Breads and cake mixes	Added, can be high	?
Slimming bars	Added, can be high	?
Powdered sauces	Added, can be high	?
Reduced fat foods *e.g.* mayonnaise and biscuits	Added, can be high	?
Some lagers	Added, can be high	?
Powdered or artificial fruit juice	Added, can be high	?
Fresh meat from the butcher	None	0
Fresh fruit	None	0
Fresh vegetables	None	0
Eggs	None	0
Pure squeezed orange juice	None	0
Lactic acid (lactate)	None	0

Note: The numbers in this table have been rounded up and thus are very approximate. ? = no accurate levels known. 1% is equivalent to about 20ml milk, a typical amount in a cup of tea, 10% to 200ml. A normal glass of milk contains about 200-250ml, a block of butter weighs 250g, and a block of cheese perhaps 250-500g. A spoonful of Parmesan cheese, freshly grated = about 30g, equivalent to 0.3g lactose or 6ml milk. Discover how much you can tolerate. Watch our web site **www.welstonpress.com** as we have set up the equipment to measure lactose in food.

claiming to be 'dark', so our chocolate recipes use genuine dark chocolate with a cocoa content of at least 70% - delicious. Don't worry too much if it says on the packet 'may contain some traces of milk'. This probably means that it has been made in a vessel that had some milk in it at some time. It may be a problem if you are allergic to milk proteins. But it is unlikely that there will be enough lactose to cause a problem if you are lactose intolerant.

When reading a food label, it is important to understand what contains lactose and what does not. Lactose is sometimes on the label, but often not. Food labelling in the USA and Finland seems better than many other countries. The EU regulations have been rather weak in this regard, and we hope that statements by the Foods Standards Agency that there will soon be a change in labelling regulations will improve the situation. To help, we have produced a simple guide in **Table 4**.

Table 4. A quick guide to food labels.

Substance on the label	Contains lactose (amount)
Lactose	Yes (100%)
Milk (cow's, goat's or ewe's)	Yes (high)
Milk powder	Yes (high)
Skimmed milk or skimmed milk powder	Yes (high)
Milk solids	Yes
Whey or whey powder	Yes (high)
Cheese	Yes (variable)
Cream	Yes
Buttermilk	Yes
Chocolate	Yes
Yoghurt	Some
Margarine	Maybe
Curd	Maybe
'Added sugar'	Maybe
Milk protein or caseinate	No (may have a little)
Glucose	No
Sucrose	No
Dextrose (should be glucose)	No
Lactate	No
Eggs or pure egg powder	No
Coconut milk	No
Coconut cream	No
Peanut butter	No

Most packaged foods are labelled with their contents - their calorific value and the amounts of protein, carbohydrate, fat and so on. Many have even more detail with amounts of saturated and unsaturated fat, vitamins, salts, specific sugars, and additives for colouring and storage. The latter are sometimes quoted as E numbers, so that the specific chemical can be looked up. Fresh food and drink such as meat, vegetables, fish, bread, and fruit juices do not have to be labelled in this way. Hence any added lactose will probably not be stated on the label. As I have already highlighted, bread and some chicken are potential danger foods if you are lactose intolerant. **Table 4** is a guide to ingredients that may be on a food label that do or do not contain lactose.

A quick look in our cupboard revealed - lactose in a French paté, dried skimmed milk in chicken nuggets, milk powder in crisps, whey powder in sponge fingers and cheese biscuits, whey powder in a frozen pizza, skimmed milk and whey powder in chocolate spread, and 'added sugar' in pickles, ketchup and squash without saying what sugar it was. All of these are potentially danger foods if you are lactose intolerant. So take care! Try and read the label, and remember not to look only for dairy, milk or lactose itself. It may be 'hidden' somewhere else.

Beware slimming bars, breakfast bars, and 'low fat' products. These can have added lactose. Jams and marmalades have lots of sucrose, but we have no evidence that there is any added lactose. Real mayonnaise should be OK. There is no lactose in spirits such as gin, whiskey, brandy, sherry or port. But lactose can be added to beers and lagers, alcopops, and even some cheap wines. Eggs have no lactose, so you can enjoy these to the full.

The calcium problem

'You must drink your milk if you want to have strong bones and teeth,' many mothers have been taught to tell their children. But do we really need the calcium in milk? There has been much debate about the recommended daily amount of calcium. One 250ml glass of milk contains about 300mg of calcium, one fifth of the daily requirement (1-2g). Some people who are lactose intolerant can obtain this by ingesting small amounts of milk throughout the day without exhibiting gut symptoms. Cheese is a good source of calcium, but will of course contain a small amount of lactose. A good portion of greens can supply 150mg of calcium. A serving of salmon or sardines contains up to 300mg. Thus it is easily possible to take the necessary daily 1-2g of calcium without milk. Soya products with added calcium are readily available in supermarkets.

In addition to the well-known allergy to certain milk proteins, allergy to at least sixteen proteins in soya milk has been found. But this is rare. However keep an eye out for this. If soya seems to produce anything from a mild rash to a severe immune reaction then you should be properly investigated, and take care not to add any soya to your diet. Alternatives to soya are lactose-reduced milk products, coconut milk, oat milk or rice milk. There is no evidence for calcium deficiency in people caused by eating a Chinese or Japanese diet with no lactose. Their bones and teeth are fine. In the West, we eat plenty of food every day, so we can easily get our daily calcium requirement. When we in the West get older, particularly women, any bone problems are likely to be hormonal rather than a direct consequence of a lack of calcium in the diet. But if you are worried when you come off milk and lactose completely please consult a doctor. And take a calcium supplement. Surprisingly calcium supplements can be cheaper than taking calcium by drinking milk. But if you can tolerate a small amount of milk, try to take your daily calcium as 'real' milk, yoghurt or cheese. Remove the added 'hidden' lactose which has little calcium benefit.

The 'double whammy'

A further problem is the presence of 'funny' sugars, found in some vegetables. The old schoolboy humour of 'beans, beans good for the heart, the more you eat the more you f✳t' has more than a ring of truth to it in fact. This is because beans, vegetables such as parsnips, chick peas and the like contain two 'funny' sugars called raffinose and stachyose. Soya also contains these.

The problem with eating a lot of these sugars is that they block the protein that absorbs glucose and galactose into the blood from the small intestine. As a result all the sugars end up in the large intestine. The bacteria here then generate hydrogen and toxic bacterial metabolites, exacerbating symptoms in patients who are lactose intolerant. Root and leguminous vegetables can contain moderate or even large amounts of these 'funny' sugars. The result is thus similar to having a low lactase enzyme when you ingest lactose. If you happen to eat a food, such as humus, that has raffinose or stachyose in it with food that has lactose then this will be a 'double whammy' for anyone who is lactose intolerant. Eating starch with raffinose or stachyose makes it worse. This is what I think happened to Stephanie when she had her major bout of illness after eating cauliflower cheese. The meal contained lots of starch and lactose, and the 'funny' sugars - her 'double whammy'.

Darwin's illness revealed

'I have had a bad spell, vomiting every day for eleven days and some days after every meal'. This is what Charles Darwin (1809-1882) (**Figure 2**) wrote in a letter to his friend Joseph Hooker in December 1863. Later he wrote to his father, a doctor himself, 'The sickness starts usually two hours after a meal'. Does this ring a bell? In fact, Darwin had already suffered chest pain and heart palpitations in December 1831 while staying in digs at Plymouth awaiting better weather for his ship the Beagle to depart. He told no one until years afterwards for fear he would not be allowed on his 'trip of a lifetime'.

Discovering lactose intolerance, and how to cope with it, has transformed my life. I am a Darwin fanatic and was absolutely staggered as I analysed the data from our first 100 patients. I realised that I had also solved one of the great mysteries in the history of science. Darwin's illness was revealed at last!

For over 40 years Charles Darwin was always ill. He saw some twenty doctors, including his father. He tried dozens of remedies, including the then famous water cure of Dr Gully at Malvern. None really worked, though Darwin did seem to improve when he underwent Gully's water therapy. This was because the only time he got better was when, by chance, he came off milk. Emma, his wife, had a recipe book. In forty eight dessert recipes, three quarters of them contain large amounts of milk or cream. Their grandfather, Dr Erasmus Darwin (1731-1802), one of the geniuses of the eighteenth century and one of the founders of the industrial revolution, recommended bread and milk for an invalid. There was a history of illness in the Darwin family. His children suffered from similar symptoms. Darwin lived in the Kent village of Down as a semi recluse because he was ill so much, sometimes for days on end. He failed to go to the famous Oxford debate in 1860, when TH Huxley got the better of Bishop Wilberforce, because he was in the middle of one of his attacks.

I have analysed Darwin's symptoms carefully. They fit exactly systemic lactose intolerance. Darwin often suffered from stomach ache, flatulence, headaches and a swimming head, vomiting, and chronic fatigue. And he frequently had joint pains, skin rashes and boils, mouth ulcers and heart palpitations. And of course he was often depressed. There has been no convincing explanation until now. But there are five pieces of evidence supporting our hypothesis that Charles Darwin suffered from lactose intolerance:

- Darwin's symptoms fit exactly those we have identified in our patients.
- The timing of his vomiting and gut pain were 2-3 hours after a meal, just as expected for lactose to reach the large intestine.
- His wife Emma used milk and cream constantly in her recipes.
- There was a clear family history in his children and on the Wedgwood side of the family.
- Darwin only got better when, by chance, he came off milk.

All that is needed now is a blood spot or a hair, and we can use our DNA test to discover whether Darwin was genetically predisposed to lactose intolerance.

Figure 2. Charles Darwin aged about 55.

Darwin did not suffer from his illness on the Beagle (1831-1836), just sea sickness and a fever in South America, probably typhoid. All sorts of ideas have been put forward to explain the illness, including arsenic poisoning, Chagas' disease and psychosomatic disorders. The latter has been favoured by several scholars in books and articles, suggesting, for example, that he had a bereavement syndrome because of the tragic death of his mother at the age of 8. Just like our patients, many doctors suggested that the problem was in Darwin's head, and, like many of our patients, he should have gone to a psychiatrist. This is nonsense!! He had an organic illness. And no wonder he got depressed when he couldn't solve his problem. How different the scientific world might be if only he had tried coming off milk. 'Hidden' lactose would not have been a problem in those days. He might never have written 'The Origin of Species'. How interesting also it is that he really missed this unique feature in the evolution of mammals. Milk has no place in 'The Origin of Species', and is only referred to fleetingly in 'The Descent of Man', his two most famous books.

'Nature takes no leaps' Darwin tells us in 'The Origin'. But was he right?

'Natural selection' is the **principle** uncovered by Darwin and Wallace, that is applied to the **process** of evolution, first described properly by Darwin's grandfather, Erasmus. Natural selection is a scientific truth. It works, and unquestionably was a major force in taking the single cells that originated 3,600 million years ago to the millions of bacteria, plants and animals that now inhabit our planet. But does 'natural selection' explain everything in evolution? I think not. In fact neither did Darwin himself, as one of the key chapters in 'The Origin' he called 'Difficulties on Theory' (1st edition) argues. These were his difficulties, not other people's hostility.

If you want to learn more about this controversy, my own 'Origin', called 'Rubicon: the Fifth Dimension of Biology' is now available from Welston Press. The intriguing question 'Rubicon' asks, and the one Darwin missed, is - 'Which came first, the enzyme lactase or its substrate lactose?' The key to understanding evolution is to discover the Rubicon crossed when both lactase and lactose could work together, and natural selection operate. The challenge is to uncover how such systems got to their Rubicon in the first place. My next book will tackle this central question to the whole of life, and medicine. And it all started in my mind when I discovered lactose intolerance!

How do I know if I have got lactose intolerance?

If you are a not an adult white Northern European then there is a high probability that you have lost most of your lactase enzyme (see **Table 1**), and thus cannot digest lactose as well as you could when you were a baby. However, as I have already said, everyone can take some milk. The only definitive way of telling whether you are really intolerant to lactose is to try a diet completely free of lactose for at least one month, maybe 3 months, including the avoidance of foods where there is a risk of 'hidden' lactose. **Table 5** is a simple guide to foods that contain lactose and those that should not. Record your symptoms before and after coming off lactose, with a severity score. If there is a dramatic improvement then stay away from lactose for the rest of your life, and enjoy the recipes in this book to the full.

However 1-3 months is a long time. It would be nice if there was a rapid medical test. Well we now have an improved one that will detect, in a couple of days, over 75% of those with lactose intolerance. The current diagnosis of lactose intolerance involves taking 50g of lactose by mouth, equivalent to 1litre of cow's milk, followed by measurement of breath hydrogen every 30 minutes for 3 hours. A breath hydrogen of 20 parts per million (ppm) above the nadir indicates lactose intolerance. We have now drastically revised this test. Our new clinical procedure has important implications for the management of IBS, chronic fatigue, and arthritis. It also has potential social and economic benefits by reducing primary care visits and prescribed drugs, and even perhaps improving assessments for life insurance. See '**The Science Bits**' for more details of our revised clinical management of lactose intolerance.

Table 5. A simple guide to food labels and foods with and without lactose.

Food	Contains lactose?
Cow's milk	Yes
Goat's milk	Yes
Ewe's milk	Yes
Whey, the liquid from milk, and powder	Yes
Skimmed milk powder	Yes
Yoghurt	Yes
Cream	Yes
Cheese	Yes
Buttermilk	Yes
Processed meats	Maybe
'Added sugar'	Maybe
Commercial milk protein	Maybe
Commercial casein (caseinate)	Maybe
Bread	Maybe
Butter	A little
Fresh organic meat	No
Fresh fish	No
Fresh sea food	No
Fresh fruit and vegetables	No
Eggs	No
Pure milk protein, e.g. casein	No
Milk fat or oil	No
Coconut milk	No
Soya milk	No
Oat milk	No
Rice milk	No

Note: See **Table 3** for the amounts of lactose in various foods and drinks.

23

Is milk bad for you?

In the medical literature there are papers claiming that milk is beneficial, and may reduce, for example, heart disease. On the other hand, there are other publications claiming that milk intake correlates with a number of diseases, including heart attacks, certain types of cancer such as breast and prostate, and even Parkinson's disease. Have a look at some of the books and papers I have referred to in the '**Further Reading**' section at the end of the book if you want more information. Look for yourself at the controversy. I still like to drink some milk every day because I am lactose tolerant.

The geologist Jane Plant has written about her remarkable story of how she survived cancer after coming off milk, and switching to a Chinese style diet. But this is just one isolated case, and is anecdotal. Milk is complex stuff. It contains many proteins, fats, salts, vitamins and a number of other small organic substances. In few studies have I found any effect of milk attributed to lactose, other than the case of lactose intolerance. The key is mechanism. Medical science can go on and on with correlation studies until we are all blue in the face. But unless biochemists like myself can come up with an explanation at the molecular level of how a particular correlation actually works we cannot move forward. This is why I believe our bacterial toxin hypothesis is so important. At last we have the basis of a real link between chemical events in the gut and physiological changes in other parts of the body. To prove this we need first to identify the molecular culprits, which we have done. Then we have to show how these can actually cause a headache, fatigue, a heart to palpitate, or an inflammatory cell to release histamine. The secret will be how the bacterial toxins affect the movement of tiny ions across the membranes that surround all our cells.

At last we now see a link to my passion for glow-worms and other amazing creatures that emit light. By using the DNA from these animals we can light up chemical processes in living cells, and discover exactly how and why people with lactose intolerance suffer their symptoms. Perhaps we can even open the door to a new era in medical research, where we can see clearly when the trillions of little bacteria in our digestive system can be friend or foe. This is for the future. If you want to learn a bit more about the science have a look at '**The Science Bits**' at the end of the book.

Coming off lactose has transformed my life and that of my family, as well as the lives of several hundred patients. They now feel wonderful, with a massive reduction in drugs and visits to the doctors, and even coming off surgery lists. Three of our patients even became unexpectedly pregnant after coming off lactose. All these people, like my own family, have been given their lives back.

This recipe book is about providing you with a new quality of life, and helping you to enjoy your meals to the full.

Bon appétit!

Alternatives to milk

Most supermarkets sell several alternatives to cow's milk for those with lactose intolerance:

1. Low lactose cow's milk e.g. Lactolite
2. Soya (soy) milk - unsweetened with added calcium, or sweetened with apple juice
3. Rice milk
4. Oat milk
5. Coconut milk

Low lactose milk is made by adding an enzyme that breaks the lactose in two, into galactose and glucose. It is thus rather sweet, though there is a recent innovation in the USA that has removed this sweetness. Our children like low lactose milk on their cornflakes. For some recipes this low lactose milk works better than soya milk, e.g. for lactose free pancakes.

Milk from soya, rice or oats is made by blending soya beans, rice or oats with water. The solids are then filtered off, leaving a white 'milk' which, because it is entirely vegetable in origin, contains no lactose at all. If you are used to cow's milk, then it takes a few days to get used to the taste. But our experience is that once you have crossed this Rubicon, you will never want to drink cow's milk again!

Other lactose free foods include:

- Tofu: This is prepared from soybeans and available in supermarkets and health food shops.
- Cream substitutes: These are prepared from vegetable oils, e.g. soya oil.
- Lactose free margarine: This is made from vegetable oil and has no added lactose, unlike some conventional margarines.
- Lactose free cheese: This is made from vegetable oil or tofu, instead of milk.
- Lactose free yoghurt: This is made from soy beans. However, some true natural yoghurts have quite a low lactose content anyway, since the bacteria have broken the milk-lactose in two. Beware artificial yoghurts which can contain added lactose.
- Lactose free ice cream: Once again this is made from vegetable oils, and is remarkably tasty. I am still experimenting to make lactose-free home-made ice cream, and my favourite Crème Brulée, with soya milk.
- Lactose free custard: This is a particular favourite with my family on apple crumble, and is made from soy beans.
- Sorbets: These are made from fruit, sugar and water, and home made will contain no lactose. But beware sorbets bought in shops or restaurants, these can contain lactose.
- Coconut milk and coconut cream.
- Fresh meat: All meat initially is lactose free, but it can be injected with lactose, or sprayed, as with some chicken. So buy from a butcher where the origin of the meat is known.
- Fresh fish.
- Fresh fruit and vegetables.
- Eggs.

Some milk substitutes can curdle when added to very hot liquids, such as a cup of coffee. Don't boil them when using them in cooking. I have found that soya milk can replace milk or cream in many classic recipes, such as white sauces and spaghetti carbonara. But soya doesn't work well in making ice cream the conventional way. However the supermarkets sell now both a soya custard and soya ice cream which are both quite tasty. Also I have found that soya milk doesn't work quite so well when making pancakes or rice pudding. I have found that you can use low lactose cow's milk instead. See the web sites listed at the end of this book for more information. Pure coconut milk or coconut cream are completely lactose free and are very tasty in Asian dishes.

What exactly is soya?

Several of the recipes in this book use soya milk instead of milk or cream. So what is soya? Is it really as good for you as cow's milk?

Soya products come from the soya plant (*Glycine max.*), originally from China. There are several varieties, but the most common one used now is the variety with yellow seeds. Soya is a leguminous plant in the family Leguminosae. This means, like the pea plant, it has pods with seeds, three in fact per pod, and it has nodules on its roots containing bacteria that can trap nitrogen and convert this into ammonia that can then be used by the plant to make proteins. Thus such plants are often used to enrich the soil. A range of products from soya are available in many supermarkets and health food shops (**Table 6**), but the one I have used in this book is soya milk. Soya milk is made by first removing the pods and husks. Then the beans are soaked, ground up and liquidised in water. The insoluble material is removed and the 'milk' heated very quickly for a short time to kill any bacteria. I find that this is still a problem, as soya milk, once opened, will only keep for few days in the fridge, often less than pasteurised milk. When you first use soya milk in tea or coffee, or on your breakfast cereal, you will immediately notice it does taste different from cow's milk. But after a few days you will find that this is the taste you prefer. The taste of cow's milk becomes the one you swallow in trepidation.

Soya belongs to a group of foods know as pulses, which include lentils. Pulses are the dried seeds of leguminous plants, and are used often in Asian cooking adding thickening and texture to the dish. Soya products play an important role in the diet in Asian countries. The soya bean is rich in protein, minerals and oil, of which nearly a quarter is unsaturated fat. Soya beans also contain a number of non-nutritional factors such as a trypsin inhibitor, sterols and isoflavones. Several of these are lost when preparing the products of soya, such as soya milk. Complicated chemicals called phytooestrogens and isoflavones are found in soya and have been claimed to have some health benefits. Populations eating a lot of soya products tend to have a lower prevalence of certain diseases, such as vascular and bone disease, and some cancers. A number of clinical studies have been published (see **'Further Reading'**) apparently showing benefits in reducing prostate and breast cancer, and in osteoporosis, kidney disease, and the menopause. Many of these beneficial effects are thought to be due to the isoflavones, or to the fact that a soya rich diet means that other perhaps harmful foods, such as those rich in unsaturated fats, are less prevalent. These hypotheses need further study, but the evidence that soya can reduce cholesterol levels has been accepted by the Federal Drugs Administration (FDA) in the USA.

Table 6. Typical soya products available in shops and supermarkets.

Soya product	What is it?	Use
Soya milk	Liquid from beans ground up in water	Cow's milk substitute in tea, coffee and recipes which normally use milk or cream
Tofu	Curd precipitated from water extract of soya beans	Bland, used in stir-fries
Texturised soya proteins	Semi pure protein from soya beans minus oil	Meat substitute for vegetarians, e.g. sausages, hamburgers
Tempeh	Cooked fermented soya beans with the mycelium of *Rhizopous oligosporous*	Chewy meat alternative
Miso	Fermented soya using *Aspergillus oryzae*	White, brown or red paste used as a base in soups and stews for texture and flavour
Soya sauce	Fermented paste e.g. shoyu and tamari	Savoury seasoning for salad dressings and meat sauces
Soya bean oil	Oil separated from ground soya beans	Blended cooking oils, margarines, crisps and salad dressings

The FDA in the USA have said that '25g of soya protein a day, as part of a diet low in saturated fat and cholesterol, may reduce the risk of heart disease'. A key finding reported at the 5th International Symposium into 'The role of soya in preventing and treating chronic disease' held in Orlando, USA in 2003 was the fact that soya significantly reduced cholesterol levels in the blood. The mechanism of these proposed effects is still to be fully elucidated. But they do support the case that including soya in a cholesterol lowering diet can be beneficial. But soya milk has only one tenth the level of calcium compared with cow's milk. So I recommend using the calcium enriched soya milk available in most supermarkets and health food stores. These are also available sweetened or unsweetened. My family prefer the latter, but the choice is, of course, yours.

Soya products can also be used successfully if you happen to be allergic to cow's milk proteins. It is possible to be allergic to the proteins in soya beans, but this is extremely rare. If you suspect an allergic reaction after ingesting soya, such as shortness of breath or itchy skin, see a doctor as soon as possible. We have yet to see a case of this.

A final issue about soya is the controversial one of Genetic Modification (GM). Soya was the first major food stuff to be made in bulk from plants that had been genetically modified, so that they were resistant to a major weed killer used all over the world to improve crop growth by killing competing weeds. All the scientific evidence is that products from these GM soya plants are safe. We do not take up DNA from plants into our bodies. Ethically it may have been unacceptable to load so much GM food on to an unsuspecting public without giving us the choice. But as a professional expert in human health and genetic engineering, I believe that most of the hot air in the Press has been simply scare mongering, and done to sell newspapers. Mutant tomatoes do not make you red in the face, unless you happen to be hot under the collar in the first place!

The GM debate is a complex one both scientifically, ethically and ecologically. I appreciate all the different views, and I am keen to be part of an informed debate. But as far as this book is concerned we all have to accept that it is virtually impossible to buy soya products that are completely GM free. I have no problem with this. It has no effect on the enjoyment of cooking and eating meals involving soya products. The rice and oat milk products may have less risk of GM contamination, but this needs confirmation.

There are companies now that can test for GM contamination if you are really worried (see the web site list at the end of the book).

Weights and measures

Many recipe books have lists of conversion tables from fluid ounces to pints, to millilitres, to litres, and from ounces to grams or from pounds to kilograms. Forget it!! Just use your common sense, your eyes and most important your taste buds. Much of this measuring in cooking is a lot of baloney. In most of my recipes I have tried to use amounts based on simple measures such as spoons and mugs. In France a teaspoon becomes a coffee spoon, of course.

Often the *exact* amounts don't matter, unlike in a scientific experiment when I weigh things out to an accuracy of at least 1%. This is part of the fun of cooking for me. When I am in the lab I am incredibly meticulous about the amounts I add in an experiment. But when I come home, and get into the kitchen, I can just lob the ingredients in. Quite relaxing really, particularly when I have a glass of chilled Chablis in my hand!!

But for completeness here are a few numbers to help you convert from British Imperial measures to Metric equivalents. Get that calculator out now. And good luck!!

1oz = 28.4g
1lb = 16oz = 0.45kg

1g = 0.04oz
100g = 3.6oz
1 kg = 2.2lb

1 pint = 0.57litre
100ml = 0.18pint
1 litre = 1.76pints

1 mug = 200-250ml or 6-8oz

Calories

If you put a spoon with sugar in it over a flame the sugar will catch fire and burn, forming carbon dioxide and water. The 'burning' produces heat. When we eat sugars like glucose or lactose we also 'burn' them. But instead of all the energy disappearing as heat, most of it is trapped in chemicals within our bodies so that this energy can be used to drive other reactions and processes. These include our beating heart, leg muscles so that we can walk or run, and our brain cells to that they fire as we think. All biological substances - sugars, fats, proteins, and so on - produce heat when they burn. The amount of heat is measured in calories. But if the substance is not 'burnt' these calories get stored instead, for example as fat. Hence we use 'calories' to calculate how much food we can eat without getting fat. I have not dealt with this controversial topic in this book. I advise you to use common sense.

Eating in moderation, and keeping fit, will keep us well with a good weight. If you are lactose intolerant, keeping off lactose will keep you alert and feeling well.

Temperature

Using a hot, medium or mild oven can be critical for some recipes. I have used °C, with conversions to °F or gas mark in all the recipes. For those of you who, like me, love to use an Aga cooker, then if the recipe uses a hot or medium oven, use the top roasting oven in your Aga. But if the recipe says use a mild oven, then use the bottom simmering oven. This is particularly good for slow cooking such as making a soup, pasta sauce or roast salmon. For completeness here is a conversion table (**Table 7**).

Table 7. Temperature conversions.

°C	°F	°F approx.	Gas mark
100	212	210	
140	284	280	1
150	302	300	2
160	320	320	3
170	338	340	
180	356	355	4
190	374	375	5
200	392	390	6
210	410	410	
220	428	430	7
230	446	450	8
240	464	465	

Note: The figures for °F are exact. But the column labelled 'approx.' is the one used throughout my recipes, and is accurate enough.

Salt

Salt is a pure mineral and so contains no lactose. We British have, for decades, added too much salt to our food. Yes it can bring out the flavour in a dish, but it can also swamp the delicate balance of flavours between meat and vegetables, or herbs. Most of the dishes in my book have added seasoning. But there is clear medical evidence now that too much salt is bad for your health. It can, for example, increase blood pressure (hypertension). So I always use 'low salt' salt. This may seem an anomaly.

Normal salt is sodium chloride. But you can buy in most supermarkets this so called 'low salt' salt, where a lot of the sodium has been replaced by potassium. I use this most of the time, and I also use unsalted butter. It has transformed my enjoyment of food. I can really taste the genuine flavours of the ingredients for the first time. I also use sea salt, that has other goodies such as iodine needed by the thyroid gland.

Pepper

Pepper comes from a plant and so contains no lactose. Freshly ground pepper adds a kick to many dishes. Many of my recipes use black pepper for this purpose. But when making a white sauce it looks much more appetizing not to have tiny black flecks all over the place, so I use white pepper in these dishes.

Herbs

Herbs are plants and so contain no lactose. They have seeds, flowers or leaves used as a flavouring in cooking, or as a source of a drug in medicine. They include sage, thyme, rosemary, basil, bay, parsley, oregano, dill, chives, winter savoury, coriander leaves and many others. Fresh herbs make such a wonderful difference in cooking and are the best. Many supermarkets now sell these in little pots. But why not start a small herb garden yourself from seed? Most can be easily grown in pots in a greenhouse, on the window sill or directly in the ground, starting from seeds obtainable for your local garden centre. I have found that bay trees, sage, rosemary, thyme, oregano, marjoram, parsley, chives and winter savoury all grow well in the UK. However basil is best bought in a pot, or grown in the greenhouse. Herbes de Provence can be bought dried as mixture of sage, rosemary, thyme and basil.

Herbs add so much flavour and texture to a dish, another reason for keeping the salt and pepper under control. And they are very useful as an attractive garnish. I keep a good stock of them in my kitchen. And they can be kept in the deep freeze, to be used when their season is over. Chives are a good example of this in winter. I hope you will enjoy the succulent flavours I have added to my dishes by using the appropriate herb.

Spices

Spices also all come from plants. They contain no lactose, but may contain the 'double whammy' sugars. Spices are aromatic powders added to give dishes an extra zing, and are, of course, particularly popular in Asian dishes. They include pepper, cloves, nutmeg, mace (the reddish outer covering from the nutmeg), cumin, coriander seeds, cardamom, curry powder, chilli and so on. They are used throughout the recipes in this book, though not as lavishly if this were an Asian cookbook. To bring out the flavour of a spice it is often necessary to fry it briefly in hot oil for a couple of minutes. But take care not to burn it.

One spice is particularly interesting from my point of view. It is called **asafoetida**. This comes from the resinous gum of a plant that comes from Afghanistan and Iran called *Ferula asafoetida*. This plant belongs to the Umbelliferae plant family, which has flower heads in the shape of an umbrella, and includes well known herbs like parsley, and poisonous plants such as hemlock. Small amounts of asafoetida are added to Asian dishes to prevent flatulence - gas. It would be fascinating to know how this spice achieves this. Does it have a chemical that blocks the bacterial metabolism of sugars like glucose or lactose? In which case, I predict that it should reduce the production of toxins from bacteria in the gut. I need to investigate this. I have not added this spice to any of our recipes at present.

Mustard

There are all sorts of mustards now available in the shops. I tend to use two main types - English and Dijon. Mustards are made by crushing the yellow seeds from the mustard plant that belongs to the cabbage family. It adds hotness and flavour to meat dishes in particular, and to egg and white sauce dishes. But do check the label. Mustards can have other additions. I have no evidence at present that any of them have added lactose. But the creamy ones in particular need checking. I have used Dijon mustard, a real discovery, for several years in my recipes with no problem for the rest of the family.

Vinegar

Vinegar has no lactose. There are a wide range of vinegars available, in addition to the classic malt vinegar used on fish and chips. These include red and white wine vinegar, cider vinegar, and the strong balsamic vinegar. The sharpness in vinegar is mainly due to acetic acid. Vinegars need to be used with care, but do add a bite to salads and many other dishes. Try keeping some in a jar with some herbs, such as rosemary or thyme. After a week or so the vinegar will have the wonderful flavour of the herb.

Fat

Fats are the greasy and oily substances that do not mix with water. Our body is full of them. Animal fat, cooking fat and cooking oils are all made up from glycerol attached to a variety of fatty acids. In the body they are liquid. But at room temperature, or on the butcher's slab, animal fat becomes a white solid. In the body, fats can be mixed up with cholesterol.

'Bad' fats tend to have fatty acids that are called 'saturated', and these are the ones that solidify easily. However oils such as olive oil, or the oils in fish such as mackerel, tend to have a higher 'unsaturated' content. These are thought to be healthier than their 'saturated' cousins. I haven't addressed this health issue here. Just use your common sense.

Clarified butter

A little warmed, melted clarified butter adds a flavour and texture when drizzled onto a salad. Clarified butter is very useful when frying anything, as it prevents it burning.

1 block (200g, 8oz) unsalted butter

1 Melt the butter carefully in a saucepan on a medium heat (or in the microwave). Do not allow the butter to brown.
2 Remove from the heat and allow the solids to settle.
3 Carefully spoon off the solids floating on the top.
4 Then pour the liquid butter into a dish. Use a spoon to prevent any of the solids on the bottom entering the dish.
5 Store in the fridge until needed.

Cheese

I love my cheese - soft or hard, cheddar, comté or camembert. But the rest of my family is very careful how much cheese they eat. As you can see from **Table 3** the lactose content in cheese is quite variable. The bacteria that convert the milk into cheese contain the enzyme ß-galactosidase

I mentioned earlier. This can split lactose into its two sugars. As a result, the cheese-making process breaks down quite a lot of the milk lactose. But of course the cheese is then compacted, concentrating the remaining components again. However many people who are lactose intolerant can eat some cheese. So you may have to experiment a little. Surprisingly perhaps, a soft French cheese like camembert is one of the lowest lactose cheeses. While the Greek cheese Feta has one of the highest lactose contents.

I often sprinkle a little Parmesan, freshly grated, on top of a gratin or quiche with no bad after effects for the rest of the family. But if you are lactose intolerant, avoid a genuine cheese dish such as cauliflower cheese or cheese fondue. These will contain too much lactose.

Olive oil versus butter

I am often asked, 'Can I still use butter as a spread?' There is very little lactose in butter, and so a small amount on bread or toast can be tolerated by most people who are lactose intolerant. In Normandy most recipes use butter, while in the South of France olive oil is preferred. Olive oil, of course, is pure oil from squeezed olives and contains no lactose.

Butter is made from milk, but contains mainly the fat, with just a little lactose. Try it and see if you can tolerate it. If you are worried then clarify the butter to remove all the non-fat material including the lactose. I use both butter and olive oil in my cooking.

Olive oil au Provence

This really is a delightful addition to salads.

> **1 mug (200ml) extra virgin olive oil**
> **2 cloves of garlic**
> **1 sprig of rosemary**
> **1 sprig of thyme**
> **3 basil leaves**
> **2 bay leaves**

1. Pour the olive oil into a saucepan.
2. Add all the other ingredients.
3. Heat until the oil just starts to bubble.
4. Take off the heat and put the lid on.
5. Leave overnight.
6. Pour the olive oil through a sieve.
7. Store in a sealed bottle.

Smell the wonderful aroma that can add extra fragrance to salad dressings and lightly cooked sauces. This can make lovely gifts too, with a strategically placed sprig of rosemary in an attractive jar, with a pretty ribbon around it.

Margarine

Beware margarines, especially 'low fat' ones, as they can contain added lactose or whey.

Vinaigrette

juice of 1 lemon
1 tablespoon of wine vinegar
salt
pepper
1 clove of garlic
1 teaspoon of Dijon mustard
1 dessert spoon of honey (optional if you want a sweeter dressing for chicken pieces)
½ mug (100ml) extra virgin olive oil

1 Squeeze the lemon juice through a sieve, to prevent pips entering the dressing.
2 Add the wine vinegar.
3 Season with salt and pepper.
4 Peel and débarrassé the garlic (remove the green, central germ that can be a little bitter).
5 Chop very finely or crush in a garlic crusher.
6 Add to the lemon juice and vinegar.
7 Mix in the Dijon mustard thoroughly.
8 Then gradually add the olive oil, mixing continuously with a whisk or fork.
9 The dressing will gradually thicken.
10 Taste and add some honey if you want to sweeten the vinaigrette.

Keep in small jug until needed. Pour over the salad at the table, otherwise the leaves will go limp quite quickly.

Marinade

Marinades always improve the flavour of meat or vegetables, particularly for barbecues. Here is a typical marinade recipe I use.

juice and zest of 1 lemon
salt
pepper
thyme
rosemary
2 cloves of garlic
1 dessert spoon of Dijon mustard
1 dessert spoon of clear honey
2 tablespoons (50ml) olive oil
½ mug (100ml) dry white wine such as a Chardonnay

1 Squeeze the lemon juice through a sieve into a mixing bowl to prevent the pips entering the marinade. These are bitter and should always be removed from any dish.
2 Peel and débarrassé the garlic (remove the green, central germ that can be a little bitter), and chop finely.
3 Season with salt and pepper and add the chopped herbs.

4   Mix in the Dijon mustard thoroughly, with the honey.
5   Add the olive oil, mixing continuously.
6   Then mix in the wine.
7   Add the meat or vegetables, and cover.
8   Leave in a bowl in the fridge to marinade for 2-3 hours, or even better overnight.
9   Remove the meat and fry in a little olive oil or on the barbecue.
10 Add the marinade after a few minutes when the meat has started to brown.

Leave out the honey if you want a marinade that is sharper. Or even add some chilli powder and soy sauce to spice it up. It is fun to experiment with different herbs, and use particular ones with different meats.

Sweet and sour sauce

1 cup of wine vinegar
1 cup of granulated sugar
½ cup of white wine
dessert spoon of soy sauce
1 clove of garlic
1 small piece of fresh ginger
1 yellow pepper
4 spring onions
salt
pepper

1   Put the vinegar and wine in a small saucepan and add the sugar.
2   Bring to the simmer to dissolve the sugar.
3   Peel and débarrassé the garlic (remove the green, central germ that can be a little bitter), and chop finely.
4   Peel the ginger and cut into long thin slices.
5   Cut the top off the pepper and remove the seeds. Cut into thin slices.
6   Add the garlic and ginger to the hot sauce.
7   Reduce by 50%.
8   Add the pepper, and simmer for a further 5 minutes.
9   Remove the roots and outer leaf from the spring onions, and chop into small pieces.
10 Add the chopped spring onions to the sauce.
11 Simmer for a further 2-3 minutes.
12 Serve immediately with crispy pork or chicken.

Serves 6 people with the crispy pork or chicken. Or you can use it to dress a hot starter.

Home made bread
Milk and bread - beware!

Many supermarket breads, and breads bought abroad such as in France, can contain both milk and added lactose. In fact the browning agent sprayed onto commercial bread often is simply a strong lactose solution. So I advise you to make your own bread. Small home baking units are available quite cheaply in most electrical retailers. I buy most of my electrical goods from our local shop - Kitchener & Thomas in Penarth, near Cardiff, who are always helpful. Have a look at the recipe book that comes with a bread maker, and count how many recipes add milk! If you make your own bread just leave out the milk from the recipe, and you can add all sorts of nice goodies, such as olives, herbs or walnuts to make the bread delicious. The principle is quite simple. All you do is make a dough with live yeast. Leave it to rise for an hour, and bake until it is brown on the outside and cooked, but still soft in the middle.

Basic bread
This makes approximately a 1kg loaf.

750g strong flour
400ml water
2 teaspoons of yeast
2 teaspoons of salt

1   Mix the yeast with some warm water and leave for 10 minutes.
2   Sift the flour and salt into a bowl.
3   Add the yeast and then the water.
4   Mix until they form a firm dough.
5   Cover the bowl with a damp cloth.
6   Leave for 30-60 minutes until the dough has doubled in size.
7   Knead the dough for 5-10 minutes.
8   Let it rise again for another 30 minutes.
9   Place in a baking dish and bake in a medium oven for 30 minutes until brown.
10 Cool and enjoy warm with some butter and home made jam.

Olive bread
Mix chopped green and/or black olives with the stones removed before baking.

Walnut bread
Mix chopped walnuts with the dough before baking.

Herb bread
Add herbs to the flour right at the beginning. A mixture of rosemary, sage and thyme works well.

❖   ❖   ❖

Many foods and drinks have milk, whey or added lactose. If the label says that the item contains a lot of sugar - beware. Some of this could be lactose!

Dos

- Always use fresh ingredients, such as meat, fish, vegetables and fruit.
- Find a friendly local butcher and fruit and veg store to help you. For our local lactose free food I use Thompson's Family Butcher, Charles Sadler's fish, poultry and game dealer, Windsor Fruit Stores, and Foxy's Delicatessen in our home town of Penarth, by the sea just west of Cardiff.
- Organic food should not have anything added to it. Jo's Organic store in Penarth is our local store.
- Prepare all food yourself, or by one of the family.
- Use soya milk, or cow's milk with low lactose, e.g. Lactolite, if you want a white sauce.
- Cook as much as possible with sunflower oil or olive oil.
- Use clarified butter if you are worried about the small amount of lactose in butter.
- Drink water, wine or pure squeezed fruit juice.
- Always check the label for added milk, cream, whey or lactose.
- When you are out at a restaurant take care. Ask if they know about lactose intolerance, and if they use dairy products or powders in their recipes. I use a number of local restaurants. The staff at our local Italian restaurant, Mediterraneos, are always helpful, and there is actually a café in the arcade in Penarth that has lactose free food on the menu. So engage with your shop keepers and restauranteurs. It is fun anyway.
- Always ask if you are not sure. If in doubt, don't eat it!
- Keep a food diary so that you can discover the culprit if you get caught out.
- When eating out tell the restauranteur or host about your lactose problem in advance, and always ask if there is any added milk or powder. If they are vague avoid it.
- Enjoy real tea or coffee black or with a slice of lemon. I have found no lactose in fruit teas.
- Keep your will power. It is so difficult when everyone else around the table is eating a delicious creamy dessert. Yet many top restaurants present fresh fruit beautifully.
- Always keep emergency supplies with you - some soya milk and water in a bottle, and fresh fruit.

dos and don'ts

Don'ts

- Avoid all processed foods, such as sausages, mordatella, salamis, and patés - unless clearly labelled 'lactose free'.
- Avoid margarines, unless shown to be lactose free.
- Avoid all powdered fruit juices.
- Avoid fruit juices not labelled as pure extract.
- Avoid all breads, unless the baker in the supermarket or in your town, or the waiter in the restaurant, can definitely tell you that no lactose has been used as a browning agent, and no milk products are in the bread mix as is often the case in white bread.
- Avoid lagers, unless they have been pre-tested to show no lactose.
- Beware 'creamy' soups when eating out.
- Beware restaurant sauces, particularly white ones, and powders used by butchers, some of which contain added lactose.
- Beware restaurant or pub roast dinners with Yorkshire pudding or vegetables with white sauces.
- Avoid all desserts with milk or cream, even sorbets, particularly if they look 'creamy', unless definitely made without milk or cream.
- Beware some instant coffee or tea powders. They can contain lactose, so read the labels carefully.
- Beware 'low fat' products as these can have added lactose.
- Avoid the 'double whammy' foods, such as humus, unless you have tested yourself.
- Don't make a fuss with your host, but never be afraid to ask.

These don'ts are absolutely vital. My family and many of our patients have been caught out many times when in restaurants in the UK, or abroad in France and Greece, when food and drink served contained added lactose without being stated on the label.

How to . . .

. . . prepare garlic

To remove the skin on a garlic clove, press down very hard on the clove with a large knife, or hit it hard. The clove will be slightly crushed and the skin will fall off easily. The clove contains a 'germ' in the centre which is slightly green and sometimes shows as a little shoot. This is bitter, and in many French recipes it is recommended to get rid of this, débarrassé as the French say, so that the bitterness (l'armertume) does not penetrate the cooking. This is particularly worth while if the garlic is to remain uncooked, as in a vinaigrette. When using garlic with onions, it is always worth softening the onions first, as the garlic tends to brown, or even burn, quickly. Reduce the heat when you add the garlic, until you add the other ingredients.

. . . finely chop onions

Cut the onion lengthways and cut off the root end. Remove the skin. Using a sharp knife make cuts lengthwise 2-3mm apart from the pointed end, not quite cutting this far. Then, with your hand holding the onion half way down, carefully make a horizontal cut parallel to the cutting surface. Finally, with your fingers curled to avoid the knife edge, hold the onion down and chop the onion finely moving down towards the pointed end. Discard the pointed end.

. . . make home made mayonnaise

Freshly made mayonnaise is always much nicer than one from a jar.

4 eggs
white wine vinegar
salt and white pepper
1½ mugs (300-400ml) good olive oil
cold water

1   Separate the eggs.
2   Whisk the egg yolks with the vinegar, salt and pepper.
3   Add the olive oil gradually, whisking all the time.
4   Add a little water at the end to thicken.

. . . make tomato mayonnaise

4 ripe tomatoes
home made mayonnaise

1   Cut a cross on the top of each tomato.
2   Soak the tomatoes in a bowl of boiling water for 2-3 minutes.
3   Remove using a slotted spoon and immediately put into ice cold water.
4   The skins will now slip off.
5   Cut the tomatoes in half and remove the seeds.
6   Chop finely and add to the mayonnaise.

How to . . .

. . . make clarified butter

If you want to fry in butter, using clarified butter prevents it burning as all the protein solids and any small amount of lactose have been removed. Simply take a block of butter and warm it gently in a saucepan until it is fully melted. With a spoon scoop off any solids floating on the top. Allow the rest of the solids to settle and pour off the butter carefully into a container.

. . . make garlic butter

5 cloves of garlic
1 pack butter (250g) salted or unsalted
juice of 1 lemon
large bunch of parsley
salt
pepper

1   Soften the butter.
2   Peel and débarrassé the garlic (remove the green, central germ that can be a little bitter). Chop finely.
3   Finely chop some fresh parsley.
4   Blend the garlic and parsley into the butter with a fork.
5   Add the juice of one lemon, being careful to sieve out all the pips. Add to the butter and mix until all the ingredients are blended together.
6   Season with salt and pepper.
7   Place on a sheet of foil and roll it to form a long cylindrical shape.
8   Cool in the fridge for several hours.

. . . make garlic bread

1   Slice into a baguette of home made lactose free bread. Take great care with shop French bread, whether you buy it in the UK or in France. It is very often made with milk powder!
2   Peel off the foil from the garlic butter and place a slice in between each cut.
3   Cover the bread with foil and warm in a medium oven (160°C, 320°F, gas mark 3) for 10 minutes until the butter has infused into the bread.

. . . make lemon and minted butter

1 pack butter (250g) salted or unsalted
bunch of fresh mint
juice of 1 lemon
salt
pepper

1 Soften the butter.
2 Finely chop some fresh mint.
3 Blend the mint into the butter with a fork.
4 Add the juice of one lemon, being careful to sieve out all the pips.
5 Add to the butter and mix until all the ingredients are blended together.
6 Season with salt and pepper.
7 Place on a sheet of foil and roll it to form a long cylindrical shape.
8 Cool in the fridge for several hours.

. . . make lemon and mint bread

1 Slice into a baguette of home made lactose free bread.
2 Peel off the foil from the butter and place a large slice in between each cut.
3 Cover the bread with foil and warm in a medium oven (160°C, 320°F, gas mark 3) for 10 minutes until the butter has infused into the bread.

. . . make melba toast

There is nothing more appetizing than a nice piece of crispy Melba toast and a little butter with your nibbles or entrée. It is very simple to prepare. Take several slices of thick bread and toast them so that they are brown on each side. Carefully cut each slice horizontally in half to make two thin slices. Place the two slices together so that the toasted sides are now facing each other in the middle. Toast again. Take care not to allow the now thin slices a chance to burn. Serve warm with paté or other starter.

. . . make breadcrumbs - french style

Many British recipes use 'wet' breadcrumbs. Once again, the French know how to do it. Dry the breadcrumbs as the French do to make chapelure. Then these absorb more fat, making the coating of chicken or potatoes more crispy than with 'wet' breadcrumbs.

1 loaf of stale home made, lactose free bread

1 Break up the bread and make into breadcrumbs in a blender.
2 Spread the breadcrumbs onto a flat baking tray.
3 Dry in a medium oven for 30-45 minutes (150°C, 300°F, gas mark 2).
4 Watch them carefully to prevent them burning.
5 Turn them every 15 minutes to allow complete drying.

The chapelure can be stored for several weeks in a dry, sealed jar in the cupboard.

How to . . .

. . . make ordinary pastry

Sift 2 mugs (400g) plain flour into a bowl. Cut up 150g butter into small pieces. Cool your hands in ice cold water. Blend the butter into the flour until it looks like breadcrumbs. Then gradually add ice cold water, mixing in with a fork and using your hands to form a firm dough. Leave to rest in the fridge for 15-30 minutes. Dust a clean work surface with flour, and roll out the pastry to just bigger than the size you want. Place in the baking dish over the meat or fruit, and spike ten times or so with a fork. Cook blind for a quiche, by placing foil over the pastry and holding it down with clean weights. Cook for 20 minutes in a medium oven at 160°C (320°F, gas mark 3).

. . . make sweet pastry

Sift 2 mugs (400g) plain flour into a bowl. Cut up 150g butter into small pieces. Cool your hands in ice cold water. Blend the butter into the flour until it looks like breadcrumbs. Sift in 5 tablespoons of icing sugar and mix in well. Beat an egg in a bowl, add the juice of one lemon and 3 tablespoons of iced water. Add the egg mix gradually to the flour, mixing in with a fork until it forms a soft dough. Firm up finally by hand and leave to rest in the fridge for 15-30 minutes. Dust a work surface with flour and roll out the pastry. Roll onto the rolling pin and place carefully where it is required.

. . . make pate sucré

This is my favourite sweet pastry. Place 150g softened butter in a bowl and work it hard with a fork until it forms a very soft, light yellow paste. Add 180g (3-4 dessert spoons) caster sugar and work into the butter to form a light creamy mix. Beat in 1-2 eggs, depending on size. Sift over 2 mugs (400g) of plain flour and fold into the sucré. Firm up finally by hand and leave to rest for 30 minutes in the fridge. This pastry is very soft and breaks easily, but can be formed into shape once in the dish. It can still be rolled on to a rolling pin, and placed where required, if you are careful.

❖   ❖   ❖

Fresh juices

Always squeeze your own orange or apple juice if you can. Juicers are quite cheap and available in most electrical stores and supermarkets.

Wines

I have become worried about lactose in cheap wines. So take care. These need thorough investigation. A small amount of lactose has been found in a small bottle of cheap wine. I will try to keep you posted through the Welston Press web site.

Beers and lagers

Take care with these. I have had it confirmed by people who previously worked in the industry that lactose can be added in quite large amounts to some beers and lagers. If they taste sweet avoid them.

Spirits

There is no lactose added to whiskey, gin, vodka, brandy or other spirits, so far as we know. So enjoy!

Aperitifs

Sherry, Muscat and rosé wines from Provence, and other aperitifs, contain no added lactose, as far as I know. My favourite summer aperitif on a sunny evening is to enjoy a really well chilled Muscat or rosé with small pieces of chopped Gallia melon - the little orangey ones, not honeydew, just as they do in Provence.

Mildly alcoholic and soft drinks

Beware alcopops and juices not made completely from squeezed fruits as these can have added lactose. Some soft drinks may also contain added lactose without being on the label.

When initially thinking about what I could cook that was completely lactose free, I found that my mind went blank.

I then had to think 'dairy', and remove all milk, cream and cheese from my recipes. Desserts were a particular problem, as so many had cream in them. I had to check lots of food labels to avoid whey and other products. I also had to think about the 'hidden' lactose problem, because of the use of lactose powder added to, or injected into, meats — especially chicken — and mustards, sauces, mayonnaise, horseradish, breads, cake mixes and biscuits. Many 'ready meals' contain some lactose, so these too were abandoned.

Eating out was a real worry, until I learned how to spot the lactose 'danger' foods. Sauces and restaurant-made desserts were a particular difficulty.

Eventually I compiled a list of over 100 recipes that I knew were 'safe', since none of the three in my family, whom I knew were sensitive to lactose, ever became 'lactosed' after eating these meals.

So here are my lactose free recipes — I hope you enjoy them as much as we do as a family. Our mealtimes have become a special daily event again, away from the TV.

Each recipe tells you approximately how long it takes from starting the preparation of the ingredients to having the dish on the table ready to eat. I have stated whether or not the dish can be frozen satisfactorily. Plus, there is a cooking or lactose tip or two with each recipe. I have also suggested what wine I have found goes well with each dish, but this, of course, is entirely up to you to enjoy experimenting!

Breakfast can be a real problem if you are lactose intolerant. Not only must you avoid milk on your cereal, but also eating toast can be a risk as bread can have milk, milk powder or lactose added to it. Also some types of fruit juices have added lactose. So always make sure you drink freshly squeezed orange juice.

Eat lactose free home made bread. Porridge made with water is a good alternative to cereal. Use organic bacon, and make sure your butcher does not add any powders containing lactose to his sausages.

And, of course, eggs, tomatoes, mushrooms and potatoes in any form are fine, except beware scrambled eggs and hash browns as these can have milk or lactose added to them.

Here are a few other suggestions . . .

tony's tip:

Pancakes without milk (see photo left and recipe opposite) - Serve immediately with sucrose sugar and freshly squeezed lemon juice, and a nice cup of Breakfast tea with soya milk. Adding a spoonful of honey or maple syrup is also delicious.

Tea and coffee

Real tea and coffee contain no lactose. And we have found no lactose so far in fruit teas. But take care with instant tea or coffee powders. These can contain lactose. Drink tea or coffee black, or with soya milk. But this needs to be added carefully to prevent the proteins denaturing. Tea does not usually curdle soya milk, but coffee often does. To prevent this, dissolve instant coffee in a small amount of water from the kettle. Add 25ml or so of soya milk to taste. Then add the rest of the hot water.

Cereal with low lactase cow's milk or soya milk

Cereals can contain added lactose so take care. This needs more investigation. Keep a look out on the Welston Press web site for more up-to-date information. But some simple cereals are OK, and can be enjoyed with low lactose cow's milk (e.g. Lactolite), soya milk, rice milk or oat milk. You can even enjoy cereal with water or fruit juice, and some sucrose sugar of course.

Fresh orange juice

This is probably the most refreshing and awakening drink in the world!

time to table - 5 minutes

1 Cool six oranges in the fridge overnight.
2 Cut in half, and juice in a juicer.
3 Remove all the pips and drink immediately.

Pancakes without milk

My children, Georgina, Emma and Lewis, insist on this favourite every Saturday morning for breakfast. I normally use low lactose cow's milk as I find it works better than soya milk. Though recently I have found that soya works OK, provided you keep the pancake moving to stop it sticking to the pan, and cook the pancake over a medium heat.

time to table - 10 minutes

1 mug (200g, 8oz) plain flour
2 eggs
2 mugs (500ml) low lactose cow's milk (*e.g.* Lactolite)
sunflower oil

1 Mix the ingredients thoroughly in a large bowl using a whisk.
2 Heat some sunflower oil in a frying pan.
3 Spoon on some pancake mix and roll it around until it thinly covers the whole surface.
4 After 2 minutes turn the pancake over, or throw it up in the air and turn it that way if you dare!

Most of the following recipes for nibbles and snacks are best made fresh and eaten the same day, and are usually not suitable for freezing.

A French classic. You need to like garlic to enjoy this. It goes beautifully with new potatoes straight from the ground, washed and cooked immediately. Aïoli is also wonderful with a rare fillet steak, or the fish from a bouillabaisse.

time to table - 10 minutes
ingredients - to serve 6-8 people

6 egg yolks
4 cloves of garlic
olive oil
salt
pepper

1 Blend the egg yolks together with a whisk.
2 Débarrassé the garlic (remove the green, central germ that can be a little bitter).
3 Finely chop and mix into the whisked egg yolks.
4 Gradually add the olive oil, whisking all the time. The final mixture should have a firm consistency.
5 Season with salt and pepper to taste.

49

tony's tip:

Make fresh, and keep cool and well-covered until required. Serve with freshly cut carrots and celery, and a chilled Chardonnay.

bruschettas

When you haven't had much lunch, and you get home really ravenous in the evening, these easy-to-make classic Italian nibbles really satisfy your appetite. Children can often be fussy eaters. But they will love these.

time to table - 10 minutes
ingredients - to serve 6-8 people

16 thick slices of home made white or lactose free bread
6 Italian tomatoes
2 cloves of garlic
1 medium sized onion
oregano
basil
olive oil
salt
pepper
grated Parmesan cheese

1. Remove the crust from the bread and cut each slice into quarters or roundels.
2. Place on a flat pan with a little olive oil on the base.
3. Then drizzle each quarter with olive oil.
4. Bake in a medium oven (160°C, 320°F, gas mark 3) for just 5 minutes, until they are just light brown.
5. Crudely chop the tomatoes and onion. You can soften the onions in warm olive oil if you wish.
6. Débarrassé the garlic (remove the green, central germ that can be a little bitter) and chop finely.
7. Mix the tomatoes, onion and garlic in a bowl and season with salt and pepper.
8. Place a spoonful of the mix carefully on each bread quarter.
9. Sprinkle with chopped oregano and basil, and then the grated Parmesan cheese.
10. Finally, drizzle a little olive oil on each portion.
11. Bake in a medium oven (160°C, 320°F, gas mark 3) for 5-10 minutes until the Parmesan starts to brown slightly.
12. Place a fresh basil leaf on each one.

Photo: see page 117

---

tony's tip:

Serve immediately with a chilled, crisp Italian white wine.

This is a simple, but tasty nibble, delicious with plenty of fresh warm toast. My family often have this with a little salad as a starter for Saturday lunch.

time to table - 12 minutes
ingredients - to serve 6 people

6 eggs
4 tablespoons of home made or shop mayonnaise (lactose free)
salt
pepper
fresh chives

1   Boil the eggs in salted water for 8 minutes.
2   Remove the shells and chop into small fragments.
3   Place in a bowl and mix with the mayonnaise.
4   Season with salt and pepper to taste.
5   Add the chopped chives.
6   Keep cool and covered until required.

tony's tip:

Serve with warm toast or Melba made from home made bread, with a light salad. But beware low fat mayonnaise, as this can have the fat replaced by added lactose.

gaucamole

Make this as spicy as you like. It makes a superb accompaniment to an aperitif. This can be stored frozen, but must be well sealed.

time to table - 10 minutes
ingredients - to serve 6-8 people

3 ripe avocados
1 small onion
2 cloves of garlic
juice and zest of 1 lemon
6 spring onions finely chopped
up to 1 teaspoon of chilli powder to taste
1 tablespoon of olive oil
salt
pepper

1   Cut the avocados in half.
2   Remove the stones and scoop the flesh into a medium sized mixing bowl.
3   Pulp with a fork or potato masher, but not too hard so that the texture is retained.
4   Chop the onion and débarrassé the garlic (remove the green, central germ that can be a little bitter) and chop very finely, and add them to the avocado.
5   Then add the spring onions, lemon juice and zest, the chilli and seasoning.
6   Mix, and add the olive oil.
7   Check for seasoning and chill.

tony's tip:

Keep the guacamole well covered with cling film to prevent the top oxidising (when it will turn a muddy brown colour). If this happens, just scrape off the top to reveal the luscious bright green of the guacamole underneath. Serve with thin slices of freshly cut carrot and celery, or Melba toast, and a well chilled Italian white wine or a Muscadet. Chardonnay is not so good with this.

This is another classic nibble, but with a difference. It goes well with an aperitif and is very simple to prepare. Leave these on the table for a few minutes when Emma is around and they will mysteriously disappear! Try crostini instead of bread and butter or toast. Toast always goes limp. But using this way of making toasties, they will stay crisp.

time to table - 12 minutes
ingredients - to serve 6-8 people

6 slices of smoked salmon
16 slices of white home made or lactose free bread
olive oil
stuffed olives

1 Using a glass tumbler or round cutter press out rings of bread, leaving the crust behind.
2 Place on a flat pan.
3 Drizzle some clarified butter or olive oil on each bread circle, and bake in a medium oven (160°C, 320°F, gas mark 3) for 5-10 minutes until crisp and slightly brown. They should be crisp on the outside and just a little soft in the centre.
4 Remove and allow to cool.
5 Place a slice of smoked salmon on each bread circle and top with half a stuffed olive.

tony's tip:

For a real treat use the expensive 'high' quality smoked salmon. It tastes so much better than the cheaper variety. And serve with a good chilled Chardonnay, such as a Chablis.

thérèse's home made tapenade

This is a classic in Provence, eaten on French bread with aperitifs. What could be better than sitting on a terrace with the sun still shining at 6 o'clock on a beautiful summer's evening in the South of France. A glass of well-chilled Provence rosé in one hand, and delicious crostini covered with tapenade in the other. We have wonderful neighbours opposite us in France. This recipe was kindly given me by the mother of the family, Thérèse, a superb cook.

time to table - 12 minutes
ingredients - to serve 6-8 people as an aperitif

8 slices of home made or lactose free white bread
1 pack (200g) green or black olives
1 onion
6 cloves of garlic
8 slices of anchovies
1 tablespoon of capers
5 tablespoons of olive oil
juice of 1 lemon (optional)
salt
pepper

1 Using a small glass or cutter cut circles out of the bread, 2-3 per slice.
2 Place on a baking tray and sprinkle with olive oil.
3 Bake in a mild oven at 150°C (300°F, gas mark 2) for 5-10 minutes until golden brown and just crisp.
4 Put aside.
5 Remove any stones from the olives.
6 Peal the onion and chop crudely.
7 Débarrassé the garlic (remove the green, central germ that can be a little bitter).
8 Put all the ingredients into a food blender and mix for several minutes until smooth.
9 No extra seasoning should be necessary.
10 Smooth a teaspoon onto each piece of toasted bread and enjoy.
11 Keep cool until required.

tony's tip:

The tapenade will keep for several weeks in a fridge. Pour a little olive oil on the top to prevent oxygen getting at the tapenade so that it keeps its colour and flavour.
Serve with a well-chilled rosé from Provence/Languedoc, such as a Lirac or Tavel.

Many of these will store well in a freezer. If soya milk is to be added then do this at the last minute, and after defrosting if you have stored the soup frozen. It takes less room in the freezer.

carrot and coriander soup

Coriander seems to be just right with carrots, complementing beautifully the sweetness of the vegetable.

time to table - 40 minutes
ingredients - to serve 6-8 people

1/3 pack (100g) clarified butter
6-8 medium to large carrots
2 small onions
1 dessert spoon of coriander powder
2-3 mugs (500ml) chicken stock
½ mug (100ml) fresh orange juice
salt
pepper
2 tablespoons fresh coriander, chopped

1 Melt the butter in a pan over a mild heat.
2 Peel and dice the carrots.
3 Soften the carrots in the butter.
4 Add the coriander powder, chicken stock and season to taste.
5 Simmer with lid on for 30 minutes until the carrots are soft.
6 Cool for 5 minutes.
7 Liquidise in a blender.
8 Add the orange juice.
9 Thin with water or more chicken stock if you wish.
10 Warm the soup and check the seasoning.

Serve with freshly chopped coriander and croutons.

tony's tip:

Try and use fresh coriander, easily available now in supermarkets.
A medium white wine goes well with this such as a Graves or other white Bordeaux, or even a white Rioja.

Another modified French classic soup. The cheese should be fine for most people who are lactose intolerant. It seems a shame not to enjoy the picture of a steaming hot soup covered with succulent melted cheese. But if you are exquisitely sensitive to lactose then leave off the cheese.

time to table - 50 minutes
ingredients - to serve 6-8 people

4-5 medium French onions (You can use British onions instead. But do not use red onions)
clarified butter
1 tablespoon of plain flour
½ bottle of French chardonnay or Sancerre white wine
1 mug (200ml) beef stock
2-3 mugs (500ml) water
1 teaspoon of granulated sugar
salt
pepper
lactose free bread
Gruyère cheese

1   Peel the onions and cut into rings.
2   Soften the onions in the melted butter until clear, being careful not to allow them to brown.
3   Add the flour and mix well.
4   Add the white wine and cook for 5 minutes.
5   Add the beef stock, the sugar, some salt and pepper.
6   Simmer for 40 minutes, and allow the alcohol to evaporate.
7   Add extra seasoning to taste.
8   Meanwhile make rings from the bread with a cutter or glass as described previously.
9   Bake in a medium oven (150°C, 300°F, gas mark 2) until slightly brown.
10 Pour the soup into a serving dish and float the crisp bread on the soup.
11 Sprinkle with grated Gruyère cheese, if you can eat a little cheese.
12 Place in the oven for 5-10 minutes to melt the cheese.

Serve immediately with the same wine as you used in the soup.

tony's tip:

Use French wine, not Australian, in the cooking as the latter is too strong in taste.
And make the croutons small, one mouthful each, as I find the large French slices often used in French onion soup are difficult to eat after they have soaked in the soup.
A fragrant, cooled Chardonnay or a Sancerre goes well. A wine from France or South America will be fine.

leek and potato soup

Well, I had to have this Welsh classic in the soup section. Make it as thick or thin as you like. It is always a lovely warming dish on a cold winter's day, with the logs burning brightly in the fire. You may not even need a main course after you have enjoyed your third helping!

time to table - 50 minutes
ingredients - to serve 6-8 people

6 medium sized leeks
1/3 pack (100g) butter
2 medium potatoes
3 bay leaves
2 large glasses (500ml) chicken stock
salt
pepper

1 Cut off the top portion and roots from the leeks. Cut a long slice in the top and wash thoroughly to remove any soil.
2 Then remove the outer layer of leaves and chop into 2cm rounds.
3 Soften the leeks for 10 minutes in the butter on a medium heat.
4 Peel the potatoes and chop into cubes.
5 Add the potatoes and soften for 5 minutes.
6 Add the chicken stock and the bay leaves.
7 Season with salt and pepper.
8 Simmer for 30 minutes.
9 Remove the bay leaves and liquidise the mixture. It will be quite thick.
10 Thin with water or more chicken stock to make the thickness you like.
11 Check the seasoning.
12 Pour through a coarse sieve or colander to remove any stringy bits from the leeks.

Serve with croutons made from lactose free bread.

> **tony's tip:**
> Don't forget to wash the leeks by cutting a slit in the top. A small amount of soil often hides here. If you use a sieve then use a coarse one rather than a fine one, as this will spoil the thick texture of the soup. But often no sieving is necessary.
> Serve with a chilled Chardonnay.

This is an extraordinary soup both in colour and texture. It is incredibly green and inviting. Use plenty of herbs as this complements the sweetness of the peas wonderfully.

time to table - 40 minutes
ingredients - to serve 6-8 people

1 kg fresh peas, or 1 large packet of frozen peas
3 cloves of garlic
fresh coriander
fresh mint
3 tablespoons of olive oil
2-3 large glasses (500ml) chicken stock
salt
pepper
water

1 Shell and boil the peas in salted water till just soft.
2 Drain the peas and blitz in a blender.
3 Peel the garlic, and débarrassé (remove the green, central germ that can be a little bitter).
4 Add to the peas, then the olive oil, and blend for 30 seconds.
5 Add the chicken stock, blend again and add the chopped coriander and mint.
6 Blend again.
7 Warm and season to taste with salt and freshly ground pepper.

Serve immediately garnished with coriander leaves and some croutons.

tony's tip:

Make sure you don't over cook the peas or they will lose their wonderful sweetness. Serve with a crisp, well-chilled Muscadet.

pepper and courgette soup

I invented this after some wild experimentation with different flavours. It has even surprised my French friends, as it has an unusual flavour and always has guests guessing about the ingredients. Take care to use fresh courgettes as these can add a bitter taste if not.

time to table - 50 minutes
ingredients - to serve 6-8 people

2 red peppers
2 green peppers
2 yellow peppers
2 medium sized courgettes
2-3 mugs (500ml) chicken stock
butter
salt
pepper
fresh parsley

1 Wash the peppers and courgettes.
2 Remove the tops and seeds from the peppers.
3 Chop roughly and soften in warm butter for about 15 minutes.
4 Add the chicken stock and simmer for a further 30 minutes.
5 Cool slightly and liquidise.
6 Strain through a sieve.
7 Season with salt and pepper.
8 Warm and garnish with a little fresh parsley.

tony's tip:

It is worth using three different coloured peppers as this adds to the colour of the soup.
Serve with croutons and a well-chilled Provence rosé. A Lirac or Tavel goes well with this.

Stephanie put this together after a visit to Tuscany. Adding bread is typical in Tuscany food. So if you can get a lactose free Italian loaf this is good.

time to table - 80 minutes
ingredients - to serve 6-8 people

2 leeks
3 carrots
2 onions
2 medium potatoes
olive oil
tin of tomatoes
2-3 mugs (500ml) chicken stock
1 tablespoon of lentils
1 tablespoon of pearl barley
1 small tin of tomato purée
salt and pepper
lactose free Italian bread

1 Remove the roots and tops from the leeks.
2 Slice a long slit in the top and wash thoroughly to remove any earth.
3 Chop the leeks into roundels and add to warm olive oil.
4 Peel the carrots and chop into roundels.
5 Peel the potatoes and chop into small cubes.
6 Peel and chop the onions.
7 Then soften them with the leeks in the olive oil.
8 Allow to soften for 5-10 minutes.
9 Add the carrots and potatoes.
10 Add the tomatoes and tomato purée, and then the stock.
11 Add the lentils and pearl barley.
12 Add a handful of the bread broken into small pieces.
13 Season with salt and pepper.
14 Simmer for 60 minutes.

tony's tip:

Make sure the bread is milk and lactose free. If in doubt make your own. This soup matures overnight. So it often tastes better the next day, as the texture and flavours soften and mingle.
Serve with a chilled Italian wine, such as Frascati, or a Tuscany red, such as a Chianti.

watercress soup

This is one of my family's Saturday lunchtime favourites. It only takes about 50 minutes and it is ready for the table. It has an amazingly delicate flavour, with a touch of spiciness from the watercress.

time to table - 50 minutes
ingredients - to serve 6-8 people

1 medium onion
½ pack (125g) clarified butter or vegetable oil
2 packets of watercress
1 dessert spoon of plain flour
2-3 mugs (500ml) chicken stock
3 bay leaves
2-3 mugs (500ml) soya milk (approx. 20g protein)
salt
pepper

1 Peel and chop the onions.
2 Soften for 10 minutes, without browning, in the melted butter or oil.
3 Add the watercress.
4 Sweat with the lid on for a further 10 minutes.
5 Add the flour.
6 Then add the chicken stock, bay leaves, salt and pepper.
7 Simmer with the lid on for 30 minutes.
8 Allow to cool slightly and remove the bay leaves.
9 Liquidise and pass through a sieve to remove gelatinous material.
10 Add the soya milk and check the seasoning.
11 Warm, but do not boil, as this can cause the soya protein to denature.

Serve immediately with croutons.

Photo: see page 118

---

tony's tip:

Always try and use absolutely fresh watercress as it will go limp if kept in the fridge for more than a day or so.
Serve with a nice bottle of chilled Chablis.

Most of these entrées are best cooked fresh and eaten immediately. I have marked the few that can be stored frozen.

aubergines farci

There is a skill in getting the flesh out of an aubergine. This can be done with the raw aubergine, but is easier if it has been cooked slightly. I have never found that the conventional trick of leaving cut aubergines with salt for 30-60 minutes makes much difference, either to the flavour or texture, though you may notice I have put this in one of the other recipes.

time to table - 50 minutes
ingredients - to serve 6 people

3 aubergines
olive oil
2 cloves of garlic
1 medium onion
oregano
rosemary
3 tomatoes
salt and pepper
Parmesan cheese

1 Wash the aubergines and cut them in half lengthwise.
2 Place them on a baking tray and drizzle a little olive oil on them.
3 Bake in a medium oven for 10 minutes until the flesh is soft when poked with a fork.
4 Remove from the oven and allow then to cool for a few minutes.
5 Meanwhile peel and débarrassé the garlic (remove the green, central germ that can be a little bitter) and chop finely.
6 Peel and chop finely the onion. Then soften in olive oil on a medium heat for 5 minutes.
7 Add the chopped garlic, oregano and chopped rosemary.
8 Cook for a further 3 minutes.
9 Skin the tomatoes by dropping them first into a bowl of boiling water.
10 Leave for 2-3 minutes. Then put them immediately into a bowl of ice cold water.
11 The skins will slip off and can be discarded.
12 Chop the tomatoes and add them to the filling.
13 Scoop out the flesh from the baked aubergines, chop and add to the mix.
14 Place the aubergine shells on a flat baking tray.
15 Drizzle a little olive oil into each one. Then fill each shell with the onion and tomato mix.
16 Season again with salt and freshly ground black pepper. Drizzle with olive oil.
17 Sprinkle with freshly grated Parmesan cheese if you are allowed.
18 Bake in a medium oven (160°C, 320°F, gas mark 3) for 30 minutes until the top is just brown.

tony's tip:

To get the flesh out of the aubergines after cutting them in half, make a cut lengthwise and several small cuts across the flesh so that this can then be scooped out easily.
Serve with a French red wine from the south of France.

The texture of a ripe avocado makes a delicious starter. But the blandness of the flavour is begging to be spruced up. I find adding hot, freshly cooked bacon pieces (lardons in France) and spring onions really spices the dish up well.

time to table - 15 minutes
ingredients - to serve 6-8 people

1 pack (250g) of unsmoked streaky bacon (lardons)
sunflower oil
3 ripe avocados
4 large tomatoes
sea salt
pepper
8 spring onions
olive oil

1 Cut the bacon into fine pieces and fry in a small amount of sunflower oil.
2 Cook slowly until crispy and keep warm.
3 Meanwhile cut the avocados in half, remove the stones and peel.
4 Place in the centre of a serving plate, carefully cut slices from the top without going fully to the top.
5 Press down to flay out the avocado.
6 Slice the tomatoes and arrange around the edge of the dish.
7 Season the whole plate with sea salt and black pepper.
8 Remove the outer layer from the spring onions and chop into small pieces.
9 When ready to serve, spoon the hot bacon onto the avocado.
10 Sprinkle with the spring onions.
11 Drizzle the whole dish with olive oil.

Serve with watercress and fresh lactose free bread.

tony's tip:

This dish is tastiest when the bacon is still warm. So keep the bacon in the pan, and sprinkle it over the avocado just before serving. If you are very sensitive to lactose then use organic bacon to be sure there has been no lactose injected into it. A crisp Italian white, such as a Soave goes well with this recipe.

chicken bites

These are so easy and quick to prepare. Ideal when you have come home after a tiring day, but still want a starter and main course. They can be ready in less than 30 minutes.

time to table - 20 minutes
ingredients - to serve 6-8 people

**1 chicken breast
salt and pepper
1 small onion
2 cloves garlic
1 yellow pepper
1 red pepper
olive oil
1 tablespoon of clear honey
splash of soy sauce
splash of white wine
unsalted cashew nuts
1 iceberg lettuce
clarified butter**

1 Remove any fat from the chicken and cut into small pieces.
2 Season with salt and pepper.
3 Finely chop the onion and garlic.
4 Remove the seeds from the peppers and cut into fine strips.
5 Put some olive oil in a frying pan and add the onion.
6 Soften till clear and then add the garlic.
7 Add the pepper strips and the chicken.
8 Then add the honey.
9 Mix well and then add the soy sauce and white wine.
10 Cook until the chicken is soft and still moist. This usually takes 5-10 minutes.
11 Place 1-2 leaves of crispy lettuce on each plate.
12 Place the chicken mix on the lettuce.
13 Spoon on a little warm clarified butter.

Serve immediately with a slice of home made lactose free bread.

> **tony's tip:**
> If the cashew nuts are salted, wash them before adding to the dish, otherwise it will be too salty. A well-chilled dry white wine, such as a Muscadet, goes well with this sweetened chicken starter.

These look scrumptious on a serving plate with their green colour, topped with the yellowish brown from the cheese complementing the sunny red of tomatoes from the previous dish.

time to table - 20 minutes
ingredients - to serve 6 people

6 courgettes
olive oil
1 clove of garlic
1 medium onion
splash of white wine
salt
pepper
Parmesan cheese

1   Wash the courgettes. Dry and cut in half lengthwise.
2   Then scrape out the flesh with a small spoon, chop and place in a bowl.
3   Lay the courgette shells on a flat baking tray.
4   Heat some olive oil over a medium heat.
5   Peel and finely chop the onion.
6   Soften in the olive oil for a few minutes.
7   Peel the garlic, débarrassé (remove the green, central germ that can be a little bitter) and chop finely.
8   Add the chopped garlic to the onions.
9   Add the chopped courgette flesh.
10 Add a splash of white wine.
11 Season with salt and pepper.
12 Cook for just 3-5 minutes.
13 Drizzle a little olive oil into the courgette shells.
14 Spoon in the mix to fill each shell.
15 Season again with a little salt and pepper.
16 Scatter a little Parmesan cheese on top if you are OK with a little cheese.
17 Bake in a medium oven (160°C, 320°F, gas mark 3) for 15 minutes.

---

tony's tip:

There is a trick to get the flesh out of a courgette cleanly without damaging the outside, but well worth the effort. First cut the courgette in half so that it will rest flat on the baking tray. Then use a small, sharp knife to cut carefully a slit lengthwise down the middle, and then several horizontal slits. Scrape out the pieces of flesh with a teaspoon.

Serve immediately with a well-chilled dry Provence, or Italian white wine, such as a Frascati.

crispy spicy chicken

This goes well as a starter or with aperitifs. The problem I have with my family is that two of us love spicy hot food, while the other three do not. The answer is to cook this dish without the chilli. Remove half of it into one serving dish, and then add the chilli to the rest. It is delicious either way, but does affect the best wine to drink with it.

time to table - 40 minutes
ingredients - to serve 6 people

2 chicken breasts
1 tablespoon of soy sauce
1 teaspoon of chilli powder
½ cup of white wine
salt
pepper
plain flour
vegetable oil

1 Wash the chicken and remove all fat and sinew.
2 Cut the chicken in to small thin slices.
3 Add the soy sauce, wine and chilli to a flat dish.
4 Add the chicken pieces, salt and pepper.
5 Turn the chicken well in the marinade.
6 Leave for 30 minutes.
7 Sift some flour into a shallow dish, and season with salt and pepper.
8 Coat the moist chicken pieces and fry, ideally in deep fat, for 2-3 minutes.
9 When crisp and light brown dry on some kitchen towel.

Serve immediately with home made tomato mayonnaise and a little salad.

> **tony's tip:**
> It is always worth placing fried meat on a piece of kitchen towel before serving. This removes any grease and keeps the meat crisp and succulent.
> If the chicken is quite spicy, a fruity white or rosé wine goes well with this dish.

This is another Saturday lunchtime favourite. Experiment with the egg mix. The filled eggs will keep in the fridge for a day or so. But make sure you cover them well as the tops will dry out and brown otherwise. They garnish a salad beautifully.

time to table - 12 minutes
ingredients - to serve 8 people

8 large eggs
1 dessert spoon of Dijon mustard
1 dessert spoon of whole grain mustard
1 tablespoon of lactose free mayonnaise
1 tablespoon of lactose free horseradish sauce
chopped chives
salt
pepper

1 Hard boil the eggs in boiling salted water for about 8 minutes.
2 Cool.
3 Remove the shells and cut in half.
4 Spoon the yolks into a bowl and make a crude powder with a fork.
5 Place the empty egg white shells on a serving plate.
6 Add the Dijon mustard, whole grain mustard, mayonnaise and horseradish to the mashed yolks.
7 Add the chopped chives.
8 Season with salt and pepper to taste.
9 Fill each egg white shell with the mix.
10 Garnish with chopped parsley.

Serve with salad dressed with a little honey vinaigrette.

Photo: see page 119

> **tony's tip:**
> Using two types of mustard adds to the texture and flavour of this dish, and prevents it tasting too sharp.
> Serve with a chilled New Zealand Chardonnay.

garlic mushrooms

Mushrooms are always a good British favourite. These are not to be confused with toadstools and other fungi, which are available in France.

time to table - 15 minutes
ingredients - to serve 6 people

500g mushrooms
3 cloves of garlic
oregano
½ pack (125g) clarified butter
2 tablespoons (50ml) dry sherry
1 tablespoon of plain flour
1 mug (200ml) soya milk
salt
pepper

1 Clean the mushrooms with kitchen paper, but do not wash them.
2 Cut into quarters.
3 Peel and débarrassé (remove the green, central germ that can be a little bitter) the garlic, and chop finely.
4 Melt the butter in a pan and add the garlic.
5 Add the mushrooms and oregano, and cook for just a few minutes. Do not overcook.
6 Add the flour.
7 Then add the sherry, and mix until the flour has absorbed the butter and sherry.
8 Add the soya milk and mix with a wooden spoon until the sauce thickens. Do not allow the sauce to boil, otherwise the soya protein will denature and the sauce will be full of bits.
9 Season to taste with salt and pepper.

Serve immediately with Melba toast made from lactose free bread.

tony's tip:
Garlic mushrooms are served so often in a sauce that is too watery. Try not to wash the mushrooms as they absorb water easily. Just clean them with a moist tea cloth or kitchen paper to remove any soil. Serve with a chilled medium dry white wine, such as an Australian Semillon.

Another family favourite. But make sure you get those really big tiger prawns if you can. Although, this dish works well with the little ones or you could use cooked prawns. Just add the prawns to the garlic and wine for a few minutes. Then remove them and put aside until the sauce is reduced by about a half. Add the prawns back just before serving.

time to table - 20 minutes
ingredients - to serve 6 people

3 cloves of garlic
2/3 pack (200g) clarified butter
2 mugs (500g) full of large uncooked prawns in their shells
zest and juice of 1 lemon
1 large glass (250ml) white wine (Chardonnay is ideal)
salt
pepper
chopped parsley

1   Peel and débarrassé (remove the green, central germ that can be a little bitter) the garlic, and chop finely. Soften in melted butter. Do not allow it to brown.
2   Add the prawns and cook gently until nicely pink.
3   Add the zest and juice of the lemon.
4   Cook for 5 minutes.
5   Then add the wine, and season to taste.
6   After 5-10 minutes of gentle cooking remove the prawns.
7   Reduce the garlic sauce by 50%.
8   Add the chopped parsley.
9   Add back the prawns and warm for 1 minute.

Serve immediately with soft lactose free bread to absorb the delicious garlic sauce.

71

tony's tip:

Don't be tempted to use cheap wine in cooking. It is always worthwhile using a wine that you like to drink anyway. And don't forget to have plenty of serviettes and finger bowls for the family and guests with which to clean their hands!
Serve with the same Chardonnay, well-chilled, that you used in the cooking.

greek salad

If you are very sensitive to lactose you may have to leave cheese out of this dish as Feta has quite a high lactose content (see **Table 3**). But this won't spoil the mix of flavours in this salad which is ideal on a hot day.

time to table - 10 minutes
ingredients - to serve 6 people

3 English onions
3 red onions
6 tomatoes
2 cloves of garlic
salt
pepper
balsamic vinegar
juice of 1 lemon
olive oil
fresh basil
Feta cheese (optional) or Parmesan

1 Peel the onions and chop into chunks. Place in the serving bowl.
2 Chop the tomatoes into quarters and add to the bowl.
3 Peel and débarrassé (remove the green, central germ that can be a little bitter) the garlic, and chop finely, and add to the mix.
4 Season with salt and pepper.
5 Sprinkle with a little balsamic vinegar.
6 Add the lemon juice.
7 Add a good quantity of olive oil and turn over the mix with your hands.
8 Chunk the Feta cheese or make shavings of Parmesan with a potato peeler.
9 Add broken basil leaves, and turn the mix again with your hands.

Serve immediately.

---

tony's tip:

Do take care not to eat too much Feta cheese if you are very sensitive to lactose, tempting as this might be. A chilled Retsina Greek wine would seem a must with this salad. Though I have to say that, in spite of much effort, many Greek wines are still not up to the quality of French and Italian wines.

The sweetness of the peppers adds so much to this light starter. But peeling them can be a nightmare. Once you have cracked this skill, you will want this dish at least once a week. It is so simple, but so, so tasty. Here I use the peppers unpeeled.

time to table - 2 hours
ingredients - to serve 6-8 people

1 large aubergine
salt and pepper
2 red peppers
2 green peppers
2 yellow peppers
olive oil
2 clusters of small tomatoes
3 cloves of garlic
zest and juice of 1 lemon and 1 lime
soy sauce
1 dessert spoon of honey
1 dessert spoon of Dijon mustard
dried oregano and dried basil

1   Wash the vegetables and dry them.
2   Slice the aubergine, place in a colander and cover with a large amount of salt. Place on a dish to collect the dark liquid that comes out. Leave for 30 minutes.
3   Wash the salt away with water and dry thoroughly with kitchen paper.
4   Cut the tops off the peppers, remove the seeds and chop into large chunks.
5   Remove the skin from the garlic, débarrassé (remove the green, central germ that can be a little bitter) and chop finely.
6   To make the marinade, put the lemon and lime juice with the zest in a large bowl.
7   Add the soy sauce, honey, Dijon mustard, salt and pepper and mix thoroughly.
8   Then add the olive oil, gradually mixing continuously with a fork until it forms a light emulsion.
9   Mix in the herbs and add the vegetables, turning them thoroughly with your hands until all are coated in the marinade.
10 Leave covered for about 1 hour.
11 Place the marinated vegetables on a roasting tray and bake in a hot oven at 180°C (350°F, gas mark 4) for 30 minutes, or until they are tender.
12 Arrange on a serving dish.
13 Add a little olive oil to the roasting dish and scrape up any juices.
14 Pour onto the cooked vegetables.

tony's tip:
Serve immediately with fresh lactose free Italian bread and a well-chilled crisp, dry Italian wine.

pembrokeshire paté

I first made this for Christmas. But with our family's love of France it has become a firm favourite throughout the year. It means the whole family can all eat paté without worrying about lactose. Many shop patés in this country and France have added milk, cream or lactose. This dish is suitable for freezing.

time to table - 3-3½ hours
ingredients - to serve 8 people, as long as you do the slicing!

1 kg (2 lb) lamb's liver
1 kg (2 lb) belly pork
3 cloves of garlic
salt and pepper
parsley
thyme leaves
2 tablespoons of brandy
pack of streaky bacon
bay leaves
juniper berries

1 Remove any skin from the belly pork, and blend well with the liver in a food mixer.
2 Peel and débarrassé (remove the green, central germ that can be a little bitter) the garlic.
3 Add the garlic, crudely chopped parsley, thyme leaves, and brandy.
4 Season well with salt and freshly ground black pepper.
5 Blend again for a few minutes.
6 Line a rectangular baking tin with foil.
7 Grease lightly and line with the streaky bacon. Then pour in the paté mix.
8 Fold over the streaky bacon and cover the top with foil.
9 Half fill a roasting tin with water and bring it to the boil.
10 Remove from the heat and carefully place into the water the baking tin with the paté in it. Take care not to scald yourself!
11 Carefully place into a medium hot oven at 170°C (340°F, gas mark 3-4) and cook for 45-60 minutes until a skewer comes out clean when inserted into the paté.
12 Cool, and put in the fridge for 2 hours.
13 Carefully remove the top foil, and use a small sharp knife to free the paté from the sides of the foil.
14 Place a serving plate on top, turn upside down and tap firmly to release the paté.
15 Decorate with two bay leaves and a few juniper berries.

Serve in slices with warm, buttered toast and a little salad garnish.

> **tony's tip:**
> Drink a Bordeaux or Chilean red wine, such as a Merlot, with this.

smoked salmon and shrimp parcels

This is quite a surprise as the hotness of the horseradish really brings out the succulence of the flavour in the smoked salmon. No extra seasoning should be necessary.

time to table - 10 minutes
ingredients - to serve 6 people

6 slices of smoked salmon
1 tablespoon of horseradish sauce (lactose free)
1 tablespoon of home made mayonnaise (shop made will do, but check the ingredients for lactose)
finely chopped dill
1 mug (200g) full of small, cooked shrimps

1 Lay out the smoked salmon slices on a serving plate and cut to make 12 small slices.

2 Mix the horseradish, mayonnaise and chopped dill in a bowl.

3 Add the shrimps.

4 Place 1 dessert spoon full of the mixture on each smoked salmon slice.

5 Wrap the salmon around the shrimp mixture.

6 Dress with a little finely chopped dill.

Serve with watercress and fresh lactose free bread.

tony's tip:
Look carefully at the label to make sure the horseradish and mayonnaise are both lactose free. If in doubt, make your own. Serve with a chilled Sancerre.

stuffed mushrooms

The key here is to keep the mushrooms moist. Don't overcook them, and use a medium oven. The nutmeg gives that extra delicious smell when cooking so that you can't wait to tuck in.

time to table - 20 minutes
ingredients - to serve 6-8 people

16 medium-sized mushrooms (or you can use giant ones)
2 cloves of garlic
2/3 pack (200g) clarified butter
1 tablespoon of plain flour
oregano
basil
parsley
3 tablespoons (50ml) dry white wine
salt and pepper
grated Parmesan cheese
freshly-grated nutmeg

1 Clean the mushrooms and remove the stalks.
2 Place the cups in a flat baking dish, and chop up the stalks finely.
3 Peel and débarrassé (remove the green, central germ that can be a little bitter) the garlic and chop finely.
4 Melt half the butter in a frying pan.
5 Add the garlic and then the chopped mushroom stalks.
6 Add the flour and allow it to absorb the butter while stirring.
7 Add the chopped or dry oregano, basil and parsley.
8 Add the wine and mix into a paste, stirring well.
9 Season with salt and pepper.
10 Add a small knob of butter to each mushroom cup.
11 Then place a spoonful of the paste into each.
12 Sprinkle with Parmesan cheese if you dare, and a little fresh nutmeg.
13 Bake in a medium oven at 160°C (320°F, gas mark 3) for 10-15 minutes until brown on top.

Serve immediately with Melba toast.

tony's tip:

Clean the mushrooms by wiping them carefully with a damp cloth or kitchen paper. Do not wash them, otherwise they will absorb water and lose their firmness when they are cooked.
Serve with a chilled Alsace or German white wine, such as a Mosel or Gewürztraminer.

Farci means 'stuffed' in French. In Provence stuffing vegetables such as tomatoes, peppers (poivrons), courgettes and aubergines is typical. Absolutely delicious. But it is worth taking the trouble to remove the seeds from the tomatoes in this dish. This removes any bitterness, and so the sweetness of the tomatoes shines through.

time to table - 30 minutes
ingredients - to serve 6 people with each one

6 medium to large tomatoes with the stalks still on
1 onion
2 cloves of garlic
4 lengths of streaky bacon
thyme
sage
rosemary
salt
pepper
olive oil

1 Cut the tops off the tomatoes and put aside.
2 Using a teaspoon remove the watery seeds from inside the tomatoes, and discard.
3 Spoon out the remaining flesh without any seeds.
4 Chop into small chunks and put into a mixing bowl.
5 Peel and finely chop the onion and garlic.
6 Soften in olive oil and add to the mixing bowl.
7 Cut the bacon into very small pieces and cook in the olive oil until nearly crisp.
8 Add to the mixture.
9 Add the chopped herbs, season with salt and pepper and add a little olive oil.
10 Place the tomato shells on a lightly oiled baking tray. If they do not stay upright cut a tiny sliver off the bottom so that each of them lies flat.
11 Drizzle a little olive oil into each shell and spoon in the mixture.
12 Bake for 20 minutes in a medium oven (160°C, 320°F, gas mark 3).
13 Then place the caps on and cook for a further 5 minutes.

Serve immediately.

> **tony's tip:**
>
> If you are in Provence there is a beautiful little cuvette of a town right on the shores of the Mediterranean called Cassis, between Marseilles and Nice. It is terribly full in summer. But up above the town there is a large car park, with buses regularly into the town centre. Here you can buy some super white, rosé and red wines which are very reasonably priced. If you can get these, then they are ideal with 'legumes farci'.
> Serve with a nice cooled, crisp rosé from Provence-Languedoc.

watercress salad

Watercress goes limp very quickly. So this dish, that can be made in minutes, must be eaten immediately. The hotness of the watercress complements the texture and taste of the avocado. While the pears give the salad that little sweetness and crunch that is so nice on a hot summer's day. Adding a little rocket also adds to the variety of this salad.

time to table - 10 minutes
ingredients - to serve 6 people

2 packs of fresh watercress
1 packet of rocket (optional)
2 ripe avocados
2 pears
olive oil
1 clove of garlic
salt
pepper
Parmesan cheese
juice of 1 lemon
fresh basil

1 Put the watercress onto a serving plate.
2 Cut the avocados into quarters, remove the stone and peel off the skin.
3 Cut into chunks and mix into the watercress.
4 Cut the pears into quarters and remove the core together with the pips.
5 Cut into thin slices and mix into the watercress with your hands.
6 Peel and débarrassé (remove the green, central germ that can be a little bitter) the garlic.
7 Chop finely and sprinkle onto the watercress.
8 Season with salt and pepper.
9 Slice shavings of Parmesan cheese using a potato peeler.
10 Mix all together with your hands.
11 When ready to serve squeeze over the lemon juice and sprinkle with olive oil.
12 Add broken fresh basil leaves.
13 Mix all together with your hands.

Serve immediately.

> **tony's tip:**
> Add the lemon juice and olive oil just before serving otherwise the watercress will go limp.
> A chilled Provence rosé, such as a Lirac or Tavel, always goes well with an entrée or nibble that has a little sweetness in it.

Most fish and seafood dishes are best cooked fresh. But some can be stored frozen.

faux coquilles st jacques

Of course you can splash out and use the real McCoy, that is scallops, in this dish. However, I have found that using white fish is very tasty, and enables you to cope with large numbers of guests quite cheaply. Hence my use of the word 'faux'. The British tend to use moist breadcrumbs made from fresh bread. This dish can be stored frozen, but is best served fresh.

time to table - 30 minutes
ingredients - to serve 6-8 people

2-3 slices of white fish (cod, hake or bass)
1 pack (250g) butter
1 medium onion
3 tablespoons of flour
½ mug (100ml) soya milk
1 mug (200ml) white wine (Chardonnay or Sancerre)
6-8 small mushrooms
salt and white pepper
chapelure (dried breadcrumbs French style)
freshly-ground nutmeg

1 Cook the fish in slightly salted boiling water for 10 minutes. Don't make it too salty as the stock will be used later.

2 Drain, retaining the stock, and put the fish aside to cool.

3 Melt 100g butter in a pan.

4 Peel and finely chop the onions.

5 Soften the onions in the butter for about 5 minutes. Put aside.

6 To make the white sauce first melt 100g butter in a pan over a mild heat.

7 Add the flour, stirring all the time until the flour makes a thick paste.

8 Add the wine, some fish stock and the soya milk, mixing constantly to keep the sauce smooth without lumps.

9 Cook until the sauce thickens. Just bring to the simmer point, being careful not to boil it or the sauce will curdle.

10 Season with salt and white pepper. Black pepper spoils the look of the sauce.

11 Break the fish into pieces, after removing any skin.

12 Place in Coquilles shells or small ramekins.

13 Add the onions.

14 Clean and thinly slice the mushrooms, and use them to cover the fish in each dish.

15 Season well with salt and white pepper and pour sauce over the top of the mushrooms.

16 Sprinkle with chapulere, and then with freshly ground nutmeg.

17 Put a small knob of butter on top of each 'shell' or pour over a little melted clarified butter.

18 Cook for 15 minutes in a medium oven (160°C, 320°F, gas mark 3).

Serve immediately with a chilled Chardonnay, such as a Chablis.

Photo: see page 120

Mackerel is a naturally oily fish and good for your heart too! Grilled, fresh mackerel doesn't really need anything to enhance it's flavour. But these extras do spice it up if you want some variety.

time to table - 30 minutes
ingredients - to serve 6 people (or according to how many fish you use)

6 fresh mackerel
vegetable oil
½ pack (125g) clarified butter
English mustard
1 teaspoon of hot chilli powder
1 dessert spoon of cumin
1 dessert spoon of ground coriander
fresh coriander leaves
salt
pepper

1 Gut and wash the mackerel. Dry with kitchen paper.
2 Cut diagonal holes in the flesh. And place on a flat tray for grilling.
3 Heat the oil in a pan and melt the butter.
4 Mix in the mustard, ground cumin, coriander and chilli powder.
5 Cook for 2-3 minutes.
6 Pour over the mackerel and stuff into the slots.
7 Leave for 10-15 minutes to allow the marinade to penetrate the fish.
8 Season with salt and pepper.
9 Grill or bake for 5-10 minutes until the flesh is cooked.
10 Sprinkle with chopped, fresh coriander leaves.

Serve immediately with watercress and a light vinaigrette.

tony's tip:
Take care with the bones in this delicious fish dish. With practise you can avoid these quite easily.
A fresh, well-cooled Muscadet will go well with this dish.

grilled tuna and salad

This is such a simple main course or starter. Tuna is a deliciously, meaty fish with a lovely texture. It should be cooked 'à point' as they say in France, *i.e.* while still red in the middle. Overcooking tuna makes it tough. My family like it as a starter served with a salad, a light, sweetish dressing and maybe a little warm, clarified butter poured over the top.

time to table - 5 minutes
ingredients - to serve 6 people

6 slices of fresh tuna
salt
pepper
clarified butter

1 Heat a skillet.
2 Season the tuna.
3 Cook on the skillet, 2-3 minutes each side.

Serve immediately with a salad dressed with honey vinaigrette.

tony's tip:

Tinned tuna is quite tasty served with a crisp salad. But once you have tasted the succulent flavour and texture of fresh tuna there will no turning back. Delicious!
A meaty fish like this deserves a richer wine than a Chardonnay. Try a Côtes du Rhône, just below room temperature.

Grilled, fresh mackerel straight from the quayside is marvellous. But this dish adds that extra interest, particularly if you want to use it as an entrée at a dinner party.

time to table - 10 minutes
ingredients - to serve 6-8 people

4 fresh mackerel
8 slices of streaky bacon
salt
pepper
olive oil

1   Fillet the mackerel, and carefully remove all the bones.
2   Cut into 16 small pieces.
3   Lightly season with salt and pepper.
4   Roll each piece in a slice of bacon.
5   Heat the olive oil in a flat pan.
6   Place each mackerel parcel carefully in the olive oil so that it first seals. Cook for just 5 minutes.

Serve immediately with watercress coated with a little warm, clarified butter, or a honey vinaigrette.

tony's tip:

After cutting out the fillets, place them on a flat board and remove the tiny vertical bones with a pair of tweezers. You don't have to be a surgeon to do this!
For a fish with such a strong flavour it is not easy to choose the right wine. But I feel that a chilled, dry white, such as a Muscadet works well. If you prefer red, then a non-fruity red, such as a Merlot is fine. A Cabernet or Syrah (Shiraz in Australia) is too strong and fruity, though a Côtes du Rhône is so flexible it is worth trying.

roasted whole salmon or salmon steaks

Whole salmon is always one of our after-Christmas dishes, when I may be catering for at least fourteen people around the lunch table. So a whole salmon goes down very well. But if there are just a few of you this dish works just as well with individual salmon steaks. The marinade is quick and easy to make, and results in a juice that can be made into a delicious sauce at the end, moistening the dish. To end up with a nice, tender and juicy salmon it is worth cooking it very slowly for a long time wrapped in foil. You can store it frozen for a week or so.

time to table - 4-5 hours
ingredients - to serve 10-12 people (for a whole salmon)

whole salmon or salmon steaks
2 cloves of garlic
1 dessert spoon of Dijon mustard
2-3 tablespoons (50ml) olive oil
salt and pepper
2 tablespoons of dill
½ bottle of Chardonnay wine
knob of butter
1 tablespoon of plain flour
1 mug (200ml) water

1 Wash the inside of the gutted salmon thoroughly, and dry with kitchen paper.
2 Line a large roasting dish with foil.
3 Place the salmon on the foil, with the gut facing upwards.
4 To make the marinade first peel the garlic and débarrassé (remove the green, central germ that can be a little bitter). Finely chop the garlic and put into a bowl.
5 Add the Dijon mustard, olive oil, dill, salt and pepper.
6 Mix into a paste.
7 Add the wine and mix again thoroughly.
8 Carefully pour the marinade into the gut of the salmon.
9 If you are using salmon steaks just place these in a gratin dish and pour over the marinade.
10 Cover the salmon with the foil, and leave for 1-2 hours, or even overnight.
11 Cook the salmon in a cool oven (140°C, 280°F, gas mark 1) for 3 hours.
12 Remove from the oven and leave to rest for a few minutes.
13 Remove the foil and place the salmon on a serving plate, pouring any juices into a bowl.
14 Add a little butter to the dish used to cook the salmon.
15 Heat on a hob.
16 Add the flour and allow it to absorb the butter, scraping any dry marinade off the dish.
17 Add the juices from the salmon, add the water and bring to the boil. Mix the sauce well, to remove any lumps.
18 Place tranches of salmon, without bones, on each plate and pour a little sauce over the top.

Serve with mashed potatoes or pommes de terre Lyonnaise, and a cooled Chardonnay, such as a nice fruity Chablis.

As a child how I dreaded fish cakes! But not any more. These fish cakes are now a firm mid-week family favourite. You can make them the day before if you like. They are suitable for freezing.

time to table - 80 minutes
ingredients - to serve 6-8 people

6-8 large potatoes
2/3 pack (200g) butter
3 tablespoons (50ml) soya milk
salt and white pepper
1 tin of cooked, pink or red salmon
1 onion
2 hard boiled eggs
1 tablespoon of chopped capers
1 tablespoon of dill
1 tablespoon of mayonnaise
plain flour
2 beaten eggs
chapulere (dried breadcrumbs French style)

1 Peel and cook the potatoes in salted water.
2 Mash with some butter and soya milk till creamy.
3 Season with salt and white pepper, and put aside.
4 Put 100g butter in a pan over a mild heat.
5 Peel and finely chop the onion.
6 Soften in the hot butter.
7 Add the onions, chopped hard boiled eggs, capers, dill and mayonnaise to the potatoes.
8 Mix and put in the fridge to cool for 30-60 minutes.
9 When cool and quite firm take a large handful and role it into a long log shape.
10 Cut into slices and dust each in flour.
11 Brush with beaten egg, and coat with the chapulere by dipping into a bowl containing the breadcrumbs.
12 Cook in clarified butter over a mild heat, or bake in the oven.

Serve with peas.

tony's tip:

It is important to allow the potato to cool and become solid before making the individual fish cakes. Otherwise you end up with most of the potato on your hands. Once again, I prefer to use the French dried breadcrumbs (chapulere) rather than breadcrumbs straight from moist bread. If freezing, then make the mixture into fish cakes first.
Serve with a light, red wine, such as a Beaujolais, slightly chilled.

smoked haddock pie

I was never that keen on fish pies, until I created this one. Smoked haddock is often yellow as a result of adding a dye. But you can now buy undyed fish from the fishmonger and supermarkets. The yellow does add colour, but I prefer to avoid such additives if possible.

time to table - 45 minutes
ingredients - to serve 6-8 people

6 eggs
4-6 slices of smoked haddock
6 large potatoes
clarified butter
2 medium onions
1 mug (200g) frozen peas
salt and pepper
dill and basil
2 tablespoons of plain flour
3-4 mugs (600ml) soya milk
1 dessert spoon of English mustard
Parmesan cheese

1 Butter a large gratin dish.

2 Cook the haddock for no more than 15 minutes in boiling, slightly salted water. Do not over salt as the stock will be used in the white sauce.

3 Drain and keep the stock. Put the haddock aside to cool.

4 Hard boil the eggs. Remove the shells when cool and cut into quarters.

5 Peel and boil the potatoes. Mash with a little butter and season to taste.

6 Add soya milk to make the mashed potatoes very smooth.

7 Peel and cut the onions into half rings. Cook over a mild heat in butter until soft and clear.

8 Skin the cooled haddock, break into small pieces and place in the gratin dish.

9 Sprinkle over the onions, and place the quartered eggs around the fish.

10 Spread the frozen peas over the top.

11 Sprinkle over the fresh or dry dill, and broken up basil.

12 Melt 100g butter in a pan.

13 Add the flour and cook until the flour grains have absorbed the butter.

14 Add the soya milk quickly to prevent the sauce going lumpy, stirring all the time, and then about a mug of fish stock. The total volume should be about ¾ litre.

15 Heat until thickened, stirring all the time. Do not allow it to boil.

16 Add the mustard. Season to taste and pour over the fish through a sieve to remove lumps.

17 Allow to cool before covering over with the smooth mashed potato using a pallet knife around the edge first.

18 Sprinkle with some grated Parmesan, if you can take a little cheese.

19 Make a pattern with a fork and add a few knobs of butter on top.

20 Cook for about 30 minutes in a medium oven (160°C, 320°F, gas mark 3) until light brown on top. Keep warm and serve with peas and a well-chilled Chablis.

You can use cooked prawns if you wish, but the uncooked ones mean that the texture of the wantons is more tender. These are nice as a starter or as a nibble before a meal.

time to table - 20 minutes
ingredients - to serve 6-8 people (2 wantons each)

20 uncooked prawns
groundnut oil
1 teaspoon of cumin powder
1 teaspoon of chilli
soy sauce
oyster sauce
2 tablespoons of dried coconut
zest of 1 orange
1 teaspoon of sugar
3 tablespoons (50ml) white wine
salt and pepper
spring onions
filo pastry
1 beaten egg

1   Heat some groundnut oil in a wok until it is very hot.
2   Add the prawns and cook for 2 minutes.
3   Add the cumin, chilli, soy sauce, oyster sauce, dried coconut, orange zest and sugar and stir well.
4   Add the wine and season well.
5   Allow the sauce to reduce without over-cooking the prawns.
6   Add the spring onions, finely chopped.
7   Place the filo pastry on a flat, clean work surface.
8   Cut the pastry into small squares.
9   Place a spoonful of the prawn mix onto each square.
10 Brush the edges of the pastry with beaten egg and fold into a small parcel, pinching the top to seal into a wanton.
11 Brush the outside with beaten egg.
12 Cook in a hot oven at 180°C (350°F, gas mark 4) for 5-10 minutes until the wantons are just beginning to brown.

Serve immediately.

tony's tip:
Appetising when served with aperitifs, or as a starter with a cup of Chinese tea.

white fish with mushroom sauce

This is such a simple fish dish, where the mushrooms complement beautifully the delicate flavour and texture of the white fish. Use Dijon mustard, as I find English mustard, that works well with some white sauce dishes, is too strong for this particular recipe.

time to table - 15 minutes
ingredients - to serve 6-8 people

1 small onion
1 clove of garlic
½ pack (125g) butter
4 fillets of cod or sea bass
2 tablespoons of plain flour
1 glass dry white wine such as a Chardonnay
1 mug (200ml) soya milk
1 dessert spoon of Dijon mustard
salt
pepper
8 small mushrooms

1 Melt the butter in a frying pan.

2 Peel and finely chop the onion and garlic.

3 Soften the onion, and then the garlic in the butter.

4 Cut the fish into 6-8 pieces.

5 Fry in the clarified butter until slightly brown on each side, some 10 minutes in total.

6 Remove the fish.

7 Add the flour.

8 When the flour has absorbed the butter, add the wine.

9 Cook for 2-3 minutes, stirring continuously.

10 Add the soya milk gradually, stirring continuously until creamy. Do not allow to boil otherwise the soya protein will denature.

11 Mix in the mustard, and season with salt and pepper to taste.

12 Clean the mushrooms with kitchen paper, and cut them in half.

13 Add the mushrooms to the white sauce.

tony's tip:

To serve, place a piece of fish on each plate. Pour over the sauce. Eat on its own as an entreé, or with peas and mashed potatoes as a main course. A chilled Australian or New Zealand Chardonnay always goes well with white fish.

Cooking these classic, Italian dishes fresh always gets the best results, and is surprisingly quick. They are never really suitable for freezing, although there are a few exceptions.

italian meat balls

This is a typical accompaniment to a pasta with a tomato ragu. The trick is to allow the meat balls to bind together so that they don't fall apart in the frying pan. Make sure the onions are quite cold before adding to the mince, and don't over-cook the meat balls, or they will become too dry.

time to table - 25 minutes
ingredients - to serve 6-8 people

1 large onion
olive oil
1kg (2lb) good mince
2 cloves of garlic
sage
thyme
salt
pepper
1 egg
½ mug (100g) chapelure (dried breadcrumbs French style)

1 Peel and finely chop the onion.
2 Heat the olive oil and soften the chopped onion until clear, being careful not to let it brown.
3 Peel and débarrassé (remove the green, central germ that can be a little bitter) the garlic.
4 Chop the garlic finely and add to the onion. Adding them after softening the onions prevents the garlic browning.
5 Allow to cool for 5-10 minutes.
6 Put the mince in a large bowl and add the chopped sage and thyme.
7 Season with salt and pepper and mix in well.
8 Mix in the now-cooled onions and garlic.
9 Finally mix in the chapelure and the beaten egg to firm up the mixture.
10 Place in a fridge for 30 minutes.
11 Then take small clumps of meat, roll into small balls and place on a dish.
12 Cook in olive oil for 10 minutes.

Serve immediately with pasta and a tomato ragu.

---

tony's tip:

It is always worthwhile allowing cooked onions to cool before adding them to mince. Otherwise the heat draws water from the meat and the meatballs won't stay intact. Any uncooked ones can be stored frozen. But don't leave them too long in the fridge as they contain uncooked egg.
Tuscany wines, such as a Chianti or a Montepulciano, go well with this dish.

This is one of my standard party dishes. It seems to go down well as there is rarely any left over! Once again you can experiment. I have found that soya milk works perfectly well in the white sauce. You can add this layer by layer, or just on the top, as you wish.

time to table - 2 hours
ingredients - to serve at least 8 people

3 onions
2 cloves of garlic
olive oil
2kg (4lb) minced beef
oregano and basil
3 carrots
½ bottle of Italian white wine
salt and pepper
3 tins of Italian tomatoes
4 hard boiled eggs
1 packet of quick cook lasagne
½ pack (125g) butter
3 tablespoons of plain flour
2 large glasses (500ml) soya milk
Parmesan cheese

To make the meat filling:
1   Peel and finely chop the onions.
2   Soften in hot olive oil.
3   Peel and finely chop the garlic.
4   Add to the onions.
5   Add the beef and cook for 10 minutes, turning constantly, until the meat is browned all over.
6   Add the oregano and basil.
7   Peel and finely chop the carrots and add to the pan.
8   Add the wine and season well with salt and pepper.
9   Cook for 5 minutes to allow the wine to develop the flavour.
10 Then add the tomatoes. Mix and cook for 1½ hours until the meat is fully tender.

To make the white sauce:
1   Melt the butter in a pan on a medium heat.
2   Add the flour and mix to make a roux, being careful not to allow the flour to burn.
3   Rapidly add the soya milk and mix thoroughly.
4   Bring nearly to boiling point and allow the sauce to thicken. Do not allow the sauce to boil as it may curdle.
5   Season with salt and white pepper to taste, and put aside.

Continued overleaf . . .

Continued . . .

To make the lasagne:

1 Using a ladle place a little meat sauce on the bottom of large, rectangular gratin dish.
2 Ladle a little white sauce on top of the meat.
3 Place a layer of lasagne on top.
4 Then repeat by ladling meat sauce, then white sauce and more lasagne.
5 In the middle layer it is quite nice to place thinly sliced hard boiled eggs.
6 Total layers should be about four or five, depending on the size of the dish.
7 Keep a little of the meat sauce and blend it briefly in a food mixer.
8 Put the remaining white sauce on top and sprinkle with freshly-grated Parmesan cheese if you are allowed this.
9 Cook in a medium oven at 160°C (320°F, gas mark 3) for 30 minutes. This will allow the lasagne to cook without becoming too limp.
10 This dish can be stored frozen, but is best eaten fresh, otherwise the lasagne becomes a little overdone.

Serve individual portions with additional meat sauce and fresh watercress.

tony's tip:

Some Italian food experts say that the classic Bolognese sauce has no added herbs. But I think that oregano and basil, classic Italian herbs, really do enrich the flavour. You can freeze the lasagne. But in this case be careful not to overcook it after it comes out of the freezer, as the pasta becomes rather soggy and loses its firmness.

A nice Chianti is lovely to drink with this dish, or even treat yourself to a 1997 Brunello di Montalcino.

My family always looks forward to an Italian supper on a Monday night, often using cold meat left over from Sunday lunch. The key to a good risotto is to ensure it stays very moist, even with liquid still visible in the dish. Most experts use proper risotto rice, but ordinary long grain rice still works. Typical risotto rice is Vialone mano, Carnaroli, or Arborio. The advantage of using this proper risotto rice is that the final dish has the beautiful creamy texture of a genuine Italian risotto. Why not try some and see if you like it better than long grain rice?

time to table - 30 minutes
ingredients - to serve 6-8 people

2 onions
2 cloves of garlic
2 carrots
1 red pepper
8 slices (250g) unsmoked streaky bacon
olive oil
500g (1lb) cold meat left-overs (roast beef, lamb, pork or chicken)
oregano and basil
salt and pepper
1-2 mugs (300-400g) long grain or risotto rice
½ bottle of Italian white wine
1 cup of beef or chicken stock depending on the meat
water
1 mug (200g) frozen peas
Parmesan cheese

1 Peel and finely chop the onions, garlic, carrots and pepper.
2 Chop the bacon and meat into small pieces.
3 Heat the olive oil in a large flat casserole dish.
4 Soften the onions and garlic for 5 minutes in the olive oil.
5 Add the chopped bacon. Then add the chopped meat.
6 Add the chopped carrots and pepper.
7 Add the herbs and cook for 10 minutes.
8 Season with salt and pepper.
9 Add the rice and allow the oil to infuse and flavour it.
10 Turn constantly to stop the rice sticking.
11 Add the white wine and allow it to infuse into the rice for 5 minutes.
12 Add the stock, and a further 2 cups of water.
13 Mix in the peas.
14 Simmer, adding water as the liquid is absorbed by the rice.

Serve topped with freshly-grated Parmesan, if you can eat cheese, and a light Italian red wine, such as a Montipulciano. Sprinkle with a little olive oil when the dish is on your plate.

Photo: see page 121

93

pesto with tagliatelle

So easy and quick to make, and you can keep the pesto in the fridge in a jar for a week or so to make a delicious pasta when you get back home from work.

time to table - 15 minutes
ingredients - to serve 6 people

3 cloves of garlic
2 dessert spoons of pine nuts
6 fresh basil leaves
½ mug (100ml) olive oil
½ mug (100g) grated Parmesan cheese
salt
pepper
tagliatelle for 6 people

1   Peel the garlic and débarrassé (remove the green, central germ that can be a little bitter).
2   Put all the ingredients in a food mixer, and blend until they form a green paste.
3   Cook the tagliatelle for a few minutes in salted water until 'al dente'.
4   Drain and turn in a little olive oil.
5   Add the pesto and turn until all the pasta is well covered.

94

Serve immediately with olive oil and freshly-grated Parmesan cheese, if you are allowed this.

> **tony's tip:**
> Add some green and/or black olives at the end to give the pasta dish some extra bite and flavour.
> Drink a chilled, dry Italian white wine with this or a Montepulciano D'Abruzzo. A Chianti or Brunello is too rich to go with this dish.

This is apparently the favourite British supper dish. Some Italian cooks will tell you that the proper bolognese sauce has no added herbs. But my family love them. Experiment and find out if you prefer this Italian classic with or without herbs. And you can experiment with other additions. Take care if you add courgettes though. It is possible to make nice pasta sauces with courgettes, but when added to meat they can go a little bitter. Let the pasta cook until just 'al dente', *i.e.* firm to the tooth. As with my other pasta sauces I have found that adding white wine to the sauce is much better than red wine, surprisingly even when using meat in the sauce.

time to table - 2 hours
ingredients - to serve 6-8 people

2 medium onions
2-3 cloves of garlic
olive oil
8 pieces (250g) unsmoked bacon
1 kg (2lb) good mince (lamb or beef)
3 carrots
dried oregano and basil
½ bottle of Italian white wine
3 tins of Italian tomatoes
salt and pepper
Parmesan cheese

1   Peel and chop the onions and garlic.
2   Soften for 5 minutes in hot olive oil.
3   Add the chopped bacon. Then add the mince.
4   Cook until the mince has browned. Add more olive oil to prevent it sticking and burning.
5   Mix in the chopped carrots, oregano and basil.
6   Add the wine, mix and cook for a further 5 minutes.
7   Season with salt and pepper to taste.
8   Add the tomatoes and cook very slowly for 60-90 minutes.
9   Then break up the tomatoes with a potato masher or fork. Check the seasoning.
10 Meanwhile add the tagliatelle to a saucepan of boiling, salted water.
11 Cook for 5-10 minutes until 'al dente'.
12 Drain and sprinkle with olive oil.
13 Mix with the bolognese sauce and leave for 5 minutes.

Serve with freshly-grated Parmesan cheese, if you are allowed this.

tony's tip:

Try making the sauce the day before. I find that the sauce matures and is even more colourful and tasty.
Serve with a good red Italian wine, such as Chianti, Montepulciano or Barolo.

This is my daughter Emma's favourite. It is very handy when I need to rustle up something quickly when she has invited some of her friends around un... ...cious with soya milk as it is with cream. The class... ...yolk in its shell!

time to table - 40 m
ingredients - to serv

1 mug full of dried l
2 medium onions
2 cloves of garlic
olive oil
8 slices of unsmoked
oregano and basil
1 tablespoon of plain
½ bottle dry Italian w
2 large glasses (500m
salt and pepper
Parmesan cheese
1 raw egg yolk each, i

1 Place the dry porcini in a small bowl and add a mug full of boiling water.
2 Leave to soak for 15 minutes.
3 Peel and finely chop the onions and garlic.
4 Heat the olive oil in a large pan.
5 Soften the onions and garlic in the olive oil for 5-10 minutes.
6 Add the chopped bacon or pancetta.
7 Cook for a further 10 minutes.
8 Mix in the oregano, basil and flour.
9 Add the white wine and cook for 5 minutes.
10 Add the softened porcini with the juices.
11 Add the soya milk and cook for a further 15 minutes. Do not allow to boil as this may lead to denaturation of the soy protein.
12 Season with salt and pepper to taste.
13 Meanwhile, add the spaghetti to a saucepan of boiling, salted water.
14 Cook for a few minutes until 'al dente'.
15 Drain and add a little olive oil to prevent the pasta sticking.
16 Mix the pasta with the carbonara sauce and leave for 5 minutes.

Serve with freshly-grated Parmesan cheese, if you are allowed this, and a medium Italian white wine or a light Italian red, such as a Valpolicella. The raw egg does add incredibly to the texture of the sauce, but is just as delicious without.

Photo: see page 122

tomato ragu with tagliatelle

If you are lucky enough to be on holiday in Italy when you make this dish, you will probably be able to get genuine, fresh Italian tomatoes. They are a revelation, sweet and juicy, so you can probably leave out the sugar. But I find that cooking at home, adding a little sugar brings out the flavour of the tomatoes, fresh or from a tin. I haven't put any fresh pasta recipes in this book. But there is a superb selection of pastas available in the shops. This dish is delicious with any of them. Changing the pasta type each time also adds variety to the dish. As I suggested in the bolognese recipe, tomato sauces seem to mature overnight, and bring out more flavour. Try it if you have the time.

time to table - 80 minutes
ingredients - to serve 6-8 people

3 medium onions
2 cloves of garlic
olive oil
oregano and basil
teaspoon of granulated sugar
½ bottle of dry Italian wine
3 tins of Italian tomatoes
touch of balsamic vinegar
salt and pepper
tagliatelle for 8 people

1 Peel and finely chop the onions.
2 Peel and finely chop the garlic.
3 Soften the onions and garlic in 3 tablespoons of hot olive oil.
4 Add the tomatoes, white wine and balsamic vinegar.
5 Mix in the sugar, the chopped oregano and basil, and season with salt and pepper.
6 Simmer gently without a lid for 60 minutes to reduce by about a quarter.
7 Break up the whole tomatoes with a fork.
8 Meanwhile add the tagliatelle to salted, boiling water.
9 Cook until 'al dente' and drain.
10 Add a little olive oil to prevent the pasta sticking together.
11 Mix the sauce with the pasta and leave for 10 minutes for the sauce to infuse.

Serve the pasta with a sprinkling of Parmesan cheese if you can eat this, and a little extra olive oil to taste.

---

tony's tip:

All pasta sauces need to absorb well into the pasta. So, unlike many British restaurants, I always mix in the sauce with the pasta several minutes before serving to allow for this. The pasta is so mouth-watering when it has absorbed all those tomato and herb flavours.

A good Tuscany wine, such as a Chianti, or even a Brunello di Montalcino, is delicious with this dish.

Roast meat dishes are best cooked fresh. But stews and some other meat dishes can be stored frozen.

Many cooks always seal their meat before cooking. This is a good idea with roast beef. But with recipes such as Lamb shanks au Provence, you want the fragrance from the herbs and vegetables to penetrate into the meat. So I suggest that it is best not to seal the meat first. Another point is that wine often adds a lot to the flavour of meat sauces. But I once made the mistake of adding white wine in the cooking stock of the lamb shanks. This does not work. It makes the sauce too acid. Good old plain water is fine!

Always buy fresh meat from the butcher. Organic meat should have no additives such as lactose. But lactose can be injected into chicken. Avoid meat coated in any powders or marinade, unless you have prepared these yourself.

My French friends used to tell me off for calling this **beef** bourguignon. This is a dish from Burgundy, and so they told me very firmly it should always be called **boeuf** bourguignon! Be that as it may, it is a delicious use of what can otherwise be quite a tough cut of beef. Cook it slowly, and for a long time. The dish is very simple to prepare, and you can leave the oven on a timer so that it is perfectly cooked when you get home for supper. And make sure you have plenty of home made bread to mop up the wonderfully rich sauce. Sadly, you will have to give the French bread a miss as this will more than likely contain lactose. This dish is suitable for freezing.

time to table - 2½ hours
ingredients - to serve 6-8 people

> **3kg (6lb) thick stewing beef in chunks 5cm across**
> **plain flour**
> **2 onions**
> **sunflower oil**
> **sage**
> **thyme**
> **3 bay leaves**
> **salt**
> **black pepper**
> **2 bottles of good Burgundy, 1 for cooking, the other for drinking!**

1 Remove excess fat from the outside of the meat.
2 Coat in seasoned flour.
3 Peel and chop the onions.
4 Soften in the oil for 10 minutes.
5 Remove the onions into a dish.
6 Add the beef and seal in hot oil for 5-10 minutes.
7 Replace the onions and add 1 bottle of Burgundy.
8 Add the herbs.
9 Stir gently.
10 Simmer for 2 hours on a very low heat or in a medium oven at 160°C (320°F, gas mark 3).
11 Season with salt and freshly-ground black pepper.
12 Thicken with a roux to your taste before serving.

Serve with mashed potatoes to absorb that lovely sauce.

> **tony's tip:**
>
> A nice red Burgundy, such as a Mercurey or a Rully, made from the Pinot Noir grape, is a must, both in the cooking and drinking.

brisket

This is an old fashioned and often forgotten cut of beef. Yet if cooked really well it is delicious both hot and cold. It is an absolute must for my Christmas cold meat table, and the stock is ideal for a tasty vegetable soup later in the week.

time to table - 4½ hours
ingredients - to serve 6 people (with plenty left over for the cold meat table)

2kg (4lb) piece of brisket held together with string
salt and pepper
sunflower oil
1 onion
1 carrot
1 clove garlic
4-6 leaves of sage
1 sprig of rosemary
3 bay leaves
1 litre of cold water
butter
plain flour

1 Season the brisket well with salt and freshly ground pepper.
2 Seal the meat on all sides in hot oil.
3 Place the meat in a large casserole pot. Add the water to just cover the meat.
4 Peel the onions and carrots, chop them crudely and then add them to the casserole.
5 Add the sage, rosemary and bay leaves.
6 Season again with salt and pepper. Place the lid on the casserole.
7 Cook in a medium oven at 160°C (320°F, gas mark 3) for 3-4 hours until the meat is very tender.
8 An Aga is absolutely ideal for this. Start it in the top roasting oven for 30 minutes. Then cook it in the bottom, simmering oven for the rest of the time.
9 Remove the meat onto a serving plate and let it rest for 5-10 minutes.
10 Meanwhile sieve off the vegetables and herbs.
11 Use the stock to make a rich gravy by heating a knob of butter in a pan. Add 2 tablespoons of plain flour. Mix in the stock. Check for seasoning. It probably won't need any.
12 Place the onions and carrots around the meat.

Serve with hot, mashed potato.

---

tony's tip:
Brisket must be cooked slowly and for a long time if you are to enjoy the soft succulent texture of the meat.
Serve with a nice red Burgundy or a Languedoc/Roussillon red wine.

This is ideal for a barbecue, but is equally delicious cooked in the oven. It is worthwhile making the marinade in the morning before you go to work. This allows all the mouth-watering flavours to penetrate the meat.

time to table - 5 hours
ingredients - to serve 6-8 people

6-8 chicken thighs with skin
2 cloves of garlic
sprigs of fresh rosemary and thyme
3 tablespoons (50ml) olive oil
1 dessert spoon of Dijon mustard
splash of soy sauce
salt and pepper
½ bottle of dry white wine (French or Italian)
2 tablespoons of plain flour
2 large glasses (500ml) water
chopped parsley and mint

1 Wash the chicken, dry with kitchen paper and place in a large flat roasting dish.
2 Finely chop the garlic after débarrassé (removing the green, central germ that can be a little bitter).
3 Strip off the leaves from the rosemary and chop them finely.
4 Pull off the tiny leaves from the stalks of the thyme sprig, and put them with the rosemary and garlic into a bowl.
5 Add the Dijon mustard, soy sauce and olive oil, and make into paste with a fork.
6 Season with salt and pepper.
7 Add the wine and mix thoroughly.
8 Pour over the chicken, cover and marinate for at least 3-4 hours, or even overnight, in a cool place.
9 Heat the oven to a relatively high temperature (180°C, 350°F, gas mark 4).
10 Cook the chicken for about 60 minutes, until the flesh is tender and the skin crispy on top. The marinade should have almost disappeared.
11 Remove from the oven, place the chicken on a serving plate and keep warm.
12 To make the sauce, place the roasting dish on a medium heat, add a little olive oil if very dry, and then add the flour, mixing it into the oil.
13 Add the water, mixing all the time and scraping the delicious dry marinade off the bottom of the pan.
14 Simmer for 5 minutes and pour the sauce into a jug, removing all the bits by passing it through a medium sieve.
15 Pour a little of the sauce over the chicken, and decorate with chopped parsley.

Serve with new potatoes coated in melted butter, fresh chopped parsley and mint, and a mild, fruity red, such as a Côtes du Rhône or American Merlot at about 16-18°C.

chicken or turkey supreme

This works best with fresh chicken or turkey. But also you can prepare a lovely dish with left-overs, just the job, as it is so easy to run out of ideas for the remains of the Christmas turkey.

time to table - 30 minutes
ingredients - to serve 6 people

4 chicken breasts or roast chicken/turkey left-overs
½ pack (125g) butter
1 onion
1 dessert spoon of oregano
2 tablespoons of plain flour
2 large glasses (500ml) soya milk
salt
pepper
150g (1/3 lb) small mushrooms

1   Remove any fat from the chicken or turkey and cut into thin strips.
2   Melt the butter in a pan.
3   Finely chop the onion and soften in the butter.
4   Add the chicken, and cook for 5-10 minutes.
5   Add the oregano.
6   Then add the flour and move around with a wooden spoon until the flour has absorbed the butter.
7   Add the soya milk, stirring continuously to prevent the white sauce forming lumps.
8   Season with salt and pepper.
9   Add the mushrooms, cleaned and sliced.
10 Cook for a further 5 minutes only.

Serve immediately with plain rice.

> **tony's tip:**
> If you use left-over turkey or chicken take care not to over-cook it, so that the meat still remains firm and moist.
> Serve with a glass of medium white wine, such as a Sauvignon Blanc.

This is a classic dish from Northern France. So you should use butter if you can. But if you prefer olive oil then no problem. The dish will still be absolutely delicious. And that sauce... Oh, la, la!! Here, I use red wine for the cooking. If it is not good enough to drink, then it is not good enough for the cooking. So never be trapped into using a bad wine in cooking, or a half open one that may have gone off. Anyway, you will want at least a glass during the preparation, or maybe even two! As with the Boeuf Bourguignon, make sure you have plenty of lactose free home made bread to mop up all that marvellous sauce.

time to table - 2 hours
ingredients - to serve 6-8 people

8 chicken drumsticks
8 chicken thighs
plain flour
salt and pepper
2 medium sized onions
3 cloves of garlic
2/3 pack (150g) clarified butter
1 pack of streaky bacon or lardons in France
8 small shallots
chopped sage, thyme and parsley
button mushrooms
1 bottle of light red Bordeaux or Burgundy wine
2 large glasses (500ml) chicken stock

1 Season the flour. Coat the chicken pieces, brown in a little melted butter, and put aside.
2 Peel and chop the onions and garlic.
3 Melt the butter in a large casserole.
4 Soften the onions and garlic for 5 minutes in the butter.
5 Add the bacon chopped in small pieces (lardons) and cook for 10 minutes.
6 Remove the bacon, onions and garlic from the pan and put aside.
7 Peel the shallots and soften for 5 minutes in the pan with a little more clarified butter. Remove and put aside.
8 Place the chicken pieces back into the casserole, off the heat.
9 Sprinkle over the onions, garlic and bacon.
10 Sprinkle over the chopped sage, thyme and parsley (including the chopped stalks).
11 Add the bottle of red wine.
12 Put on the lid and simmer for about 1hour until the chicken is tender.
13 Add chicken stock if the sauce is too thick.
14 Add the shallots and mushrooms (cleaned).
15 Cook for a further 10 minutes.

Serve with Lyonnaise potatoes or a gratin, and a light Bordeaux wine, such as a St Emilion, or a Burgundy, such as Nuit St Georges or a Rully, depending on the wine used in the coq au vin.

grilled fillet or sirloin steak

Well, my children do have expensive tastes, and always go for the fillet in a restaurant. But a good rump or sirloin (faux fillet in France) is just as tasty, if not quite so tender. If you eat a lot of fillet steak it is well worth while asking your butcher for a whole fillet. This can save you quite a bit of money in the long run. I like my steak rare, but the rest of the family prefer it medium rare. So you have to watch each piece carefully for timing. And do let them rest for a few minutes or so before tucking in. In France, however, I tend to go for safety when ordering steak and have it 'à point'. 'Saignant' in France is often so rare it is hardly cooked at all, and is only really edible if it is fillet steak of the highest quality!

time to table - 10 minutes
ingredients - to serve 6-8 people (serves as many as you have pieces of steak, or until the wine runs out!)

250-500g (¼ to ½lb) steak per person
Dijon mustard
salt
black pepper

1 Remove excess fat from the fillet, but leave the fat on if you are using sirloin.
2 Sprinkle both sides with salt and freshly ground black pepper.
3 Coat each side with Dijon mustard.
4 Grill on a skillet - 2½ minutes each side for rare, 3½ minutes for medium, and however long you like if you want the steak tasting of old boots!
5 Allow to rest for 3 minutes.
6 Meanwhile to make a small sauce, add a little flour to the skillet, and then some water.
7 Mix with a wooden spoon until the sauce thickens.
8 Season to taste with salt and pepper.
9 Pour into a small jug.

Serve with Lyonnaise potatoes or a gratin.

Photo: see page 123

---

tony's tip:

Here, as with the roast beef, the key discovery for me was Dijon mustard. It turns what would otherwise be a rather bland steak into a juicy succulent one, each piece of steak melting in the mouth.
Serve with a good Bordeaux red wine, such as a St Julien or Margaux.

You can't beat good Welsh lamb. Here again a coating of Dijon mustard adds to the flavour of the meat and the sauce. I like the fat really crispy, so you may have to experiment with your oven to achieve this, while still keeping the meat juicy and tender.

time to table - 45 minutes
ingredients - to serve 6-8 people

8-12 lamb chops
1 dessert spoon of Dijon mustard
2 cloves of garlic
1 sprig of fresh rosemary
salt
pepper
olive oil
plain flour

1 Brush both sides of the lamb chops with Dijon mustard, or, if you don't mind getting your hands messy, coat them by hand.
2 Place the lamb chops in a lightly oiled roasting dish.
3 Peel and débarrassé (remove the green, central germ that can be a little bitter) the garlic.
4 Finely chop the garlic and sprinkle it over the chops.
5 Then sprinkle them with finely chopped rosemary.
6 Season with salt and pepper.
7 Pour a little oil over each chop.
8 Cook in a hot oven at 180°C (350°F, gas mark 4) for 30-40 minutes.
9 When cooked, place the lamb on a serving plate.
10 Add 2 tablespoons of flour to the roasting dish and mix well over heat.
11 Add water and mix to form a smooth sauce.
12 Season well with salt and pepper.
13 Sieve the sauce into a jug.
14 Pour a little of the sauce over the chops and decorate with fresh rosemary.

Serve immediately with Lyonnaise or mashed potatoes.

tony's tip:

Don't over-cook small chops or they will end up too dry.
Serve with a good red Burgundy, such as a Mercurey, Rully or Nuit St Georges.

lamb shanks au provence

This is a classic Provence dish, modified slightly, that you will find on offer on many lunchtime blackboards when you sit down at any small restaurant in one of the medieval towns that make Provence so enduring. A Provence rosé is a must with this dish.

time to table - 3 hours
ingredients - to serve 6 people (or as many shanks as you cook)

6 lamb shanks
2 medium sized onions
4 carrots
3 sticks of celery
large sprigs of rosemary, thyme and parsley
4 sage leaves
1 litre of water
salt and pepper
100g (a knob) of butter
2 tablespoons of plain flour

1   Place the lamb shanks into a large casserole pot.
2   Cut the onions in half, peel and slice into half rings.
3   Peel the carrots and cut into chunks.
4   Cut the celery into 2-3 cm lengths. Add to the pot with the onions and carrots.
5   Put the rosemary, thyme, sage and chopped parsley around the shanks. Fresh herbs are best.
6   Season well with salt and pepper.
7   Pour the water over so it just covers the meat.
8   Bring to the boil and simmer on the hob or in a mild oven (150°C, 300°F, gas mark 2) for at least 2-3 hours. The lamb should be cooked very slowly so that when served it just falls off the bone, beautifully moist and tender.
9   Remove the shanks and place on a serving dish. Decorate with small sprigs of rosemary and thyme.
10 Drain the liquid through a crude sieve or colander and put aside. Remove the cooked carrots and celery, and place around the meat. Some people discard the cooked vegetables, but they can be a delicious addition to the meat.
11 In a saucepan, melt the butter on a medium heat. Make a roux with the flour, mixing it in with the butter to prevent burning. Add the liquid from the meat, and mix to form a rich sauce. Season with salt and pepper to taste.
12 Pour a little over the meat, and serve the rest in a jug or sauceboat.

Serve the meat with the vegetables.

---

tony's tip:
Use mashed potatoes to allow you to mop up the delicious sauce. Serve with a light Bordeaux, such as a St Emilion, a Burgundy such as a Rully, or even a South American Merlot.

This really is a lovely rich stew, wonderful with mashed potatoes to mop up the sauce. It lasts for days in the fridge, unless eaten first time to the table! It is suitable for freezing.

time to table - 1½ hours
ingredients - to serve 6-8 people

6 lamb cutlets
flour
salt and pepper
sunflower oil
2 medium onions
2 cloves of garlic
3 parsnips
3 carrots
4 small turnips
½ swede
6 tomatoes
1 small tin of tomato purée (make sure this is lactose free)
1 mug of red wine
rosemary and sage
2 tablespoons of ground paprika
2 large glasses (500 ml) meat stock

1 Cut the lamb into medium sized chunks.
2 Coat them in seasoned flour.
3 Seal in hot oil for 5-10 minutes in a large casserole.
4 Peel and finely chop the onions and garlic.
5 Add to the lamb and cook for 5 minutes.
6 Peel and chop the parsnips, carrots, turnips and swede.
7 Add them to the casserole.
8 Then add the chopped tomatoes.
9 Pour over the wine and mix in the tomato purée.
10 Mix in the chopped rosemary, sage and the paprika.
11 Pour in the stock.
12 Season well with salt and pepper.
13 Bring to the simmer.
14 Cook in the oven for 1hour at 170°C (340°F, gas mark 3-4) until the lamb is tender.

Serve with mashed potatoes.

> **tony's tip:**
> Adding the tomatoes and paprika gives this dish that extra richness not always present in a conventional British stew.
> Serve with a Burgundy, such as a Côtes du Beaune or Nuit St Georges.

pork chops with herbs & garlic and bread sauce

The key to this dish is to cook the chops well, but to keep them moist and tender. There is nothing worse than an overdone pork chop! I love pork crackling. But it is very difficult to get the crackling really crispy, and at the same time not to over-cook the chop. So I don't usually bother.

time to table - 3 hours
ingredients - to serve 6 people

zest and juice of 1 lemon
salt and pepper
fresh thyme, tarragon and parsley
2 dessert spoons of Dijon mustard
olive oil
6 large pork chops without the rind
1 bulb of garlic
4 parsnips
6 medium to large potatoes
breadcrumbs
wine vinegar
water

To prepare the marinade and chops:
1　Place the lemon juice and zest in a large bowl.
2　Add salt and pepper, and the chopped herbs, dried will be fine if fresh aren't available.
3　Mix the Dijon mustard in well.
4　Add one clove of finely chopped garlic.
5　Then add 3-4 tablespoons (50ml) olive oil and mix thoroughly.
6　Add in the chops and coat well, rubbing the marinade into the meat firmly with your hands.
7　Place the chops on a large, flat baking tray.
8　Wash and dry the parsnips and potatoes.
9　Cut the parsnips into quarters and remove the woody centre.
10　Cut the potatoes into 1cm thick slices.
11　Add the vegetables to the marinade.
12　Break up the bulb of garlic. Remove excess skin and add to the marinade.
13　Mix well with your hands and pour onto the chops. Arrange so that the chops are on the top. Leave to marinade for 1-2 hours if possible.
14　Cook in a hot oven at 200°C (390°F, gas mark 6) for 1hour.
15　Remove the chops when they are cooked.

To prepare the bread sauce:
1　Make breadcrumbs from half a loaf of home made lactose free bread.
2　Add freshly chopped thyme and tarragon. Dried herbs are not very good here.
3　Add 4 tablespoons of olive oil and mix well into a paste.
4　Add 1 tablespoon of wine vinegar with a little water and mix further into a nice rich paste.

Serve with the chops and a glass of Burgundy or Languedoc red wine.

Veal is now difficult to obtain from butchers here in Britain. But it is easy to get in France or Italy. So maybe you will have to wait for your holiday to use the real McCoy. Pork tenderloin well beaten out is a perfectly good substitute. It is a chance to use those dried herbs you bought in France last summer. You just can't beat the aroma of food when it is being cooked with herbes de Provence. Mouth-watering!

time to table - 10 minutes
ingredients - to serve 6 people

olive oil
1½kg (3lb) of pork tenderloin or veal escalope
salt
pepper
1 clove of garlic
1 dessert spoon of herbes de Provence
zest and juice of 1 lemon

1 Flatten the meat into thin slices 5-10cm wide.
2 Season with salt and pepper.
3 Heat the olive oil in a frying pan and soften the chopped garlic for 2-3 minutes.
4 Add the meat and sprinkle with herbes de Provence.
5 Cook for 5 minutes.
6 Turn the meat, and add the zest and juice of the lemon.
7 Cook for a further 2-3 minutes.

Serve immediately with a crisp, green salad.

109

tony's tip:

If you have access to fresh thyme, rosemary, basil, and sage, then why not try making your own herbes de Provence? The aroma when you chop these fresh herbs is ecstatic.
Serve with a rich Provence rosé, well-chilled, such as a Lirac or Tavel.

pork tenderloin au provence

Pork tenderloin is reasonably priced and beautifully tender. Try to cook it so that it is just pink in the middle. If you over-cook this cut of meat it can become rather tough. The final result looks really appetising covered with herbs, and the sauce is absolutely delicious.

time to table - 45 minutes
ingredients - to serve 6 people (depending on tenderloin size)

1 pork tenderloin
1 clove of garlic
2 dessert spoons of Dijon mustard
fresh rosemary, sage, thyme and basil
salt and pepper
olive oil
1 onion
1 tablespoon of flour

To prepare the meat:

1 Carefully remove all the fat and sinew from the tenderloin, and put aside in a flat dish.
2 Peel and débarrassé (remove the green, central germ that can be a little bitter) the garlic.
3 Chop very finely and place in a bowl.
4 Add the Dijon mustard, chopped herbs, salt and pepper. Mix into a paste.
5 Spoon the paste over the pork and cover the meat completely using your hands.
6 Leave to rest for 30 minutes.
7 Cook the pork for just 10 minutes in olive oil, turning it every 2 minutes or so.
8 Remove from the pan and allow the meat to rest for a few minutes.
9 Place the whole tenderloin on a flat surface and cut into slices 1-2cm thick. These should be pink in middle.
10 Arrange slices neatly on a serving dish. Cover with a little sauce. Sprinkle with basil leaves.

To prepare the sauce:

1 Add a little more olive oil to the pan in which the meat was cooked.
2 Peel and finely chop the onion, and add it to the pan. Cook for 2-3 minutes.
3 Add the flour, mixing continuously.
4 When the flour has absorbed the oil add 1 large glass (250ml) water.
5 Bring to the boil stirring continuously with a wooden spoon and scrapping off any cooked herbs and meat into the sauce. Season to taste with salt and pepper.
6 Sieve into a jug and use immediately.

Serve with Lyonnaise potatoes or potato croquets coated with ground almonds.

---

tony's tip:

For Pork au tarragon, just use tarragon instead of the sage, rosemary and basil.
A Provence rosé, such as a Tavel or Lirac, goes well with this, or try a Chilean Merlot.

Ask anyone in France, or anywhere for that matter, to name **the** most famous British dish. Roast beef and Yorkshire pudding is surely it! But here I made one of my major cooking discoveries - using Dijon mustard. This adds terrific flavour to the meat, and produces wonderful gravy. Crucial also was that fact that soya milk works just as well as cow's milk in the Yorkshire pudding. A good cut of meat is vital. Also sealing the meat before roasting, and leaving it to rest before carving is essential for a superb result. A rich Bordeaux wine is wonderful with this dish.

time to table - 1 hour
ingredients - to serve 6-8 people

1 large cut of beef such as topside or on the bone
2 tablespoons of Dijon mustard
salt and pepper
sunflower oil
2 tablespoons of plain flour
2 large glasses (500ml) water
for the Yorkshire pudding:
½ mug (120g, 4oz) plain flour
2 eggs
1 mug (200ml) soya milk
salt
sunflower oil

1   Season the meat and coat it generously with Dijon mustard using your hands.
2   Seal the meat in hot oil for 10 minutes, turning so that it is sealed all over.
3   Place in a roasting tin and roast in a hot oven at 190°C (370°F, gas mark 5) for 45 minutes.
4   Remove on to a serving plate and allow it to rest for at least 5-10 minutes.
5   The meat when cut should be beautifully pink in the middle and brown at the edges.
6   Drain most of the fat from the roasting pan and place over a medium heat.
7   Add the flour and mix well to allow it to absorb the fat.
8   Add the water and scrape any meat off the bottom of the pan.
9   Keep well stirred with a wooden spoon until the gravy has thickened.
10 Season with salt and pepper to taste, and sieve into a jug and keep warm until needed.

For the Yorkshire Pudding (start 10 minutes before meat is taken from the oven):
1   Mix the flour, eggs and soya milk thoroughly with a whisk.
2   Season with salt only, no pepper.
3   Fill the cups of a multiple cake tray half full with oil.
4   Place in the hot oven, raising it to 200°C (390°F, gas mark 6).
5   Take the tray out of the oven when the oil is piping hot. Take care not to spill it on yourself.
6   Using a ladle, pour the pudding mix into each cup until the oil just reaches the top.
7   Cook in a hot oven at 200°C (390°F, gas mark 6) for 10 minutes or until the puddings have risen and are crispy on top.
8   Remove from the oven. The individual puddings should slip out easily.

spicy beef curry

Everyone likes a good curry. Coconut milk is ideal, and the correct ingredient. Beware, many Indian restaurants in the UK are using cream and milk in their sauces instead of coconut milk, which naturally is completely lactose free. This dish is suitable for freezing.

time to table - 30 minutes
ingredients - to serve 6 people

2 slices of sirloin or rump steak
1 onion
groundnut oil
coriander powder
curry powder or paste
4 medium tomatoes
zest and juice of 1 lime
1 tin of coconut milk
salt
pepper
pinch of nutmeg
fresh coriander
noodles

1 Remove any fat from the steak and cut into thin slices.
2 Peel and finely chop the onion.
3 Soften in hot groundnut oil, but do not allow to brown.
4 Add the steak and cook for 5 minutes.
5 Add the coriander powder, the curry paste, and the chopped tomatoes.
6 Mix and then add the juice and zest of the lime.
7 Finally stir in the coconut milk.
8 Cook for a further 10 minutes.
9 Season with salt and pepper.
10 Add the nutmeg.
11 Add the chopped fresh coriander leaves just before serving.
12 Add the noodles to a pan of boiling water.
13 Remove from the heat and leave to stand for 5 minutes.
14 Drain the noodles.
15 Place the noodles on a serving plate and pour the curry over the top.

Serve immediately.

> **tony's tip:**
> A weak Indian or Chinese tea is the best complement to this dish, allowing you to have a wonderful 'fin de bouche' that builds up after each mouthful.

A pseudo Asian recipe for variety. Make it as spicy as you like, or dare! This can be stored frozen.

time to table - 15 minutes
ingredients - to serve 6 people

4 chicken breasts
1 onion
2 cloves of garlic
groundnut oil
1 green chilli
1 red chilli
1 teaspoon of chilli powder
soy sauce
oyster sauce
½ mug (100ml) white wine
salt
pepper
6 spring onions

1   Clean the fat off the chicken breast and cut into thin strips.
2   Peel and finely chop the onion and garlic.
3   Soften these in hot oil.
4   Then add the chicken.
5   Remove the seeds from the chillies and chop finely.
6   Add to the chicken.
7   Then add the soy and oyster sauce, and the white wine.
8   Add more chilli powder if you like it really hot and spicy.
9   Season with salt and pepper.
10 A minute or two before serving, add the chopped spring onions.

Serve immediately.

Photo: see front cover and page 124

tony's tip:
Serve with either plain or turmeric rice, and some refreshing Chinese tea.

stir-fry chicken

A really quick supper dish, ready in minutes. You can vary the quantities to suit your own taste.

time to table - 20 minutes
ingredients - to serve 6-8 people

6 chicken breasts
3cm length of fresh ginger
groundnut oil
1 medium onion
2 cloves of garlic
splash of soy sauce
splash of oyster sauce
½ mug (100ml) white wine
salt
pepper
1 pack of bean sprouts
4 spring onions

1 Wash the chicken breasts, dry with kitchen paper and remove all the fat and sinew.
2 Cut diagonally into thin slices.
3 Peel the ginger and cut into thin slices.
4 Heat the groundnut oil in a pan.
5 Peel and finely chop the onions and soften them in the oil.
6 Peel and finely chop the garlic.
7 Add the garlic and ginger to the onions.
8 Then add the chicken, soy and oyster sauce.
9 Mix well while cooking.
10 Season well with salt and pepper.
11 After 5 minutes add the wine.
12 When virtually ready, add the bean sprouts and spring onions, chopped.
13 Cook for only a further 2-3 minutes.

Serve with white rice or even turmeric rice.

tony's tip:

To keep the vegetables beautifully crisp, only cook for a few minutes at the end in very hot oil.
Serve with Chinese tea (a Jasmine tea or a dilute Lapsang Souchong is nice, very hot).

Sweet and sour is always a favourite when having a Chinese take away, so I thought I would try it at home. Here is the result. Pork or chicken work equally well. Serve with Chinese tea.

time to table - 45 minutes
ingredients - to serve 6 people

1 pork tenderloin or 3 chicken breasts
salt and pepper
2 dessert spoons of soy sauce
1 cup of plain flour
1 cup of corn flour
1 cup of water
vegetable oil
For the sweet and sour sauce:
1 cup of wine vinegar
1 cup of granulated sugar
½ cup of white wine
1 dessert spoon of soy sauce
1 clove of garlic
1 small piece of fresh ginger
1 yellow pepper
4 spring onions
salt and pepper

To prepare the meat:

1   Remove any fat or sinew from the meat, and cut into small pieces about 2-3cm square.
2   Place in a flat dish. Season with salt and pepper and sprinkle with soy sauce. Set aside for 15-30 minutes.
3   Place the plain flour and corn flour in a bowl, season with salt and pepper and gradually add a cup of water, whisking continuously.
4   Continue until the flour mixture forms a thick batter.
5   When ready to cook, dip each piece of meat in the batter twice.
6   Deep fry for a few minutes until crisp.
7   Serve immediately with the sweet and sour sauce and plain or turmeric rice.

To prepare the sweet and sour sauce:

1   Pour the vinegar and wine into a small saucepan. Add the sugar and soy sauce.
2   Bring to the simmer to dissolve the sugar.
3   Peel the garlic, débarrassé and chop finely.
4   Peel the ginger and cut into long thin slices.
5   Cut the top off the pepper and remove the seeds. Cut into thin slices.
6   Add the garlic and ginger to the hot sauce. Reduce by 50%.
7   Add the slices of pepper, and simmer for a further 5 minutes.
8   Remove the roots and outer leaf from the spring onions, and chop into small pieces.
9   Add the chopped spring onions to the sauce.
10 Simmer for a further 2 minutes. Serve immediately with the meat.

recipe photographs

On the following pages:

p117   **bruschettas** A delicious appetiser, with a little crunch, that can be made simply in minutes when you get home starving after a hard day at work. (**See recipe on page 50**)

p118   **watercress soup** This is a delicious, light starter for a dinner party. But also a great start to a long, drawn out French-style Saturday lunch. (**See recipe on page 62**)

p119   **devilled eggs** A marvellous way to spice up eggs. Soft and succulent, with a crisp salad as a starter, the devilled centre gives the eggs that little bite for a summer's lunch. (**See recipe on page 69**)

p120   **faux coquilles st jacques** A great entrée after a light soup. The crisp topping and that hint of nutmeg wonderfully complements the soft texture and flavours of this dish. (**See recipe on page 80**)

p121   **left-over risotto** Such a simple way of making that left-over chicken or lamb into a delicious supper. Imagine the aromas, as the garlic and herbs blend in with the wine. There won't be much left-over after the children have tucked into this. (**See recipe on page 93**)

p122   **spaghetti carbonara** No problem with lactose in this dish! The soya milk blends perfectly with the bacon, herbs and porcini sauce, producing a symphony of flavours. (**See recipe on page 96**)

p123   **grilled fillet steak** Wow! Don't you just love that rare, succulent steak? Bet you can't wait to tuck into one of these. (**See recipe on page 104**)

p124   **spicy chicken and turmeric rice** The vibrant splash of colours from the peppers and the chicken, combined with the rich yellow of the rice, really make this dish mouth-watering as it arrives at the table. (**See recipes on pages 113 and 152**)

p125   **dad's sausage meat 'thing'** Served hot or cold, this dish really is delicious served with a tangy tomato chutney. Great when you have a big family party at Christmas. (**See recipe on page 134**)

p126   **quiche sans crème** Perfect for a relaxing Saturday French-style lunch, when just warm and served with a crisp green salad, dressed with a soft vinaigrette. (**See recipe on page 136**)

p127   **pommes de terre lyonnaise** Once you have tasted this potato dish you won't want any other. The onions add that touch of sweetness. Sprinkled with a garnish of a little chopped parsley, it really does liven up the supper table beautifully. (**See recipe on page 145**)

p128   **stir-fry vegetables** These are delicious on their own, but superbly enhance a simple meat dish, such as pork tenderloin au Provence. The blend of colours and the sweet, softness of the leeks and peppers contrast wonderfully with the crispness of the carrots. (**See recipe on page 148**)

p129   **chocolate torte sans crème** When you slice open this torte, the soft runny centre of the chocolate looks just amazing. The fantastic texture and hint of lime is an experience not to miss! (**See recipe on page 163**)

p130   **lemon sorbet** So simple, yet so refreshing, and completely lactose free! This sorbet is absolutely superb as a taste freshener after a fish entrée. (**See recipe on page 166**)

p131   **oranges in brandy syrup** A truly refreshing dessert to serve after a large meal. The brandy syrup complements the sweet succulence of the oranges marvellously. (**See recipe on page 167**)

p132   **strawberries in cointreau** What a marriage! This wonderful liqueur was just made for strawberries. A really sensuous conclusion to a lactose free dinner party! (**See recipe on page 171**)

Recipe: see page 50

bruschettas

118

watercress soup   **Recipe:** see page 62

Recipe: see page 69

devilled eggs

faux coquilles st jacques   **Recipe:** see page 80

121

Recipe: see page 93

left-over risotto

122

spaghetti carbonara

Recipe: see page 96

Recipe: see page 104

grilled fillet steak

124

spicy chicken and turmeric rice   **Recipes:** see pages 113 & 152

125

Recipe: see page 134

dad's sausage meat 'thing'

126

quiche sans crème

Recipe: see page 136

127

Recipe: see page 145   pommes de terre lyonnaise

stir-fry vegetables   **Recipe:** see page 148

129

Recipe: see page 163 chocolate torte sans crème

lemon sorbet

Recipe: see page 166

131

Recipe: see page 167

oranges in brandy syrup

132

strawberries in cointreau **Recipe:** see page 171

Many of these can be frozen. But make sure they are well wrapped up so that they retain their freshness when you eventually thaw them.

Take care when buying the ingredients as there are several that can contain 'hidden' lactose. For example, some processed meats, including sausage meat, can contain added powders with lactose. Ask your butcher to make real sausage meat without any added powders. Our local family butcher Thompson's in Penarth is very obliging in this regard. If you use beer to make a sauce, for example in the steak and kidney pie recipe, avoid lagers and stouts as these can contain lactose. Addition of lactose in the fermentation of milk stout was patented as long ago as 1910, and there are several web sites that sell lactose for this purpose.

New or mashed potatoes, with a green salad or a tomato salsa, go well with many of the pies and quiches. Individual roasted garlic cloves also add that extra touch of sweetness and interest.

As far as wine is concerned, a Beaujolais, a light Burgundy, such as an Irancy or Rully, or a Medoc from Bordeaux are all nice. A Merlot from Provence/Languedoc also goes well. A Chablis or other Chardonnay is equally nice if you prefer white wine. Experiment to see which you like best. It is worthwhile serving the wine at the right temperature: 5-8°C for a white, 13-15°C for a Burgundy or Provence wine, and 18°C for a Bordeaux. On a hot summer's day, it may be a good idea to cool the red wine just a fraction before serving.

dad's sausage meat 'thing'

If you ask my children what is the most important dish I make at Christmas, then this is it! It is known affectionately as Dad's sausage meat 'thing'! The recipe here allows a large family to have a good helping when hot, with plenty left over for the Christmas cold meat table. Make sure you store it in the fridge so that you can enjoy it for several days. Warm it up slightly when required.

time to table - 1½ hours
ingredients - to serve at least 8 people (plus several cold meals)

11 eggs
3-4 onions
3 cloves of garlic
sunflower oil
3kg (6lb) fresh sausage meat (lactose free - no powders)
sage, parsley and thyme
½ home made loaf of breadcrumbs (lactose free)
salt and pepper
400g savoury pastry

1 Hard boil 8 eggs in salted water for 8 minutes. Cool. Remove the shells and put aside.

2 Peel and finely chop the onions. Soften in warm oil.

3 Peel, débarrassé (remove the green, central germ that can be a little bitter) the garlic and chop finely.

4 Add the garlic to the onions. Put aside to cool.

5 In a large bowl, mix the sausage meat with the breadcrumbs using your hands.

6 Add the onions and garlic when cool enough to handle.

7 Mix well with the sausage meat. Add the chopped herbs.

8 Season with salt and freshly ground black pepper, and mix well.

9 Add 2 beaten eggs to help it bind together.

10 Roll out the pastry so that it is equivalent to more than the diameter of the pie you want.

11 Grease a large flat baking tray. Place the pastry on the tray, then add the sausage meat mix.

12 Shape it only roughly at this stage.

13 Make a trough in the sausage meat and place the eggs along it in a tightly fitting line.

14 Cover over with the meat mixture and make it smooth all over.

15 Fold over the pastry and seal with a little beaten egg.

16 Pierce the whole thing well with a fork and brush with a beaten egg.

17 Bake in a medium hot oven at 170°C (340°F, gas mark 3-4) for 45 minutes until golden brown.

Serve in thick slices, hot or cold, with jacket potatoes and a tasty, rich, tomato pickle. A light red wine, such as a Beaujolais or Valpolicella goes well with this. It is essential in recipes like this to use fresh sausage meat, and to ask your butcher not to add any seasoning powders, as these and many shop sausage meats can contain lactose.

Photo: see page 125

This is a simple supper time dish when you have a large party that has turned up unexpectedly that afternoon. But make sure someone helps with peeling the potatoes!

time to table - 1 hour
ingredients - to serve 8 people

8-10 large eggs
6-8 medium sized potatoes
½ pack (125g) butter
3 medium sized onions
2 tablespoons of chopped oregano
2 tablespoons of plain flour
1 carton (750ml) soya milk
1 dessert spoon of English mustard
Parmesan cheese

1　Hard boil the eggs. Cool. Remove the shells, and put aside.
2　Peel and chop the potatoes into large chunks.
3　Boil in salted water for just 10 minutes until soft on the outside but still firm in the middle.
4　Melt the butter in a pan.
5　Peel the onions and cut into half rings.
6　Soften in the butter.
7　Add the oregano, and then the flour.
8　When the flour has absorbed the butter add the soya milk.
9　Mix continuously to prevent lumps.
10　Heat until it is about to bubble, and the sauce is smooth. Do not boil as this will cause the soya protein to denature, and the sauce will separate. If this happens then sieve it before adding to the eggs.
11　Add the mustard if you like, as this gives the sauce an extra bite.
12　Cut the potatoes into small pieces, and place in a large gratin dish.
13　Cut the eggs into quarters and place them carefully over the potatoes.
14　Pour over the sauce.
15　Sprinkle with grated Parmesan cheese, if you are allowed this.
16　Bake in a medium to hot oven at 160°C (320°F, gas mark 3) for 30 minutes until the top is nice and brown and the sauce is bubbling.

Serve immediately with warm, lactose free, home made bread.

> **tony's tip:**
> Oregano always goes well with mushrooms and eggs. If you only have dry oregano then this works fine. But if you can grow it in your garden even better. The English mustard gives the sauce that extra bite. Serve with a glass of Sauvignon Blanc.

quiche sans crème

This is Emma's Saturday lunchtime favourite, served with potatoes fresh from the garden in the summer, or jacket potatoes in the winter. And a crisp salad covered with a mild vinaigrette. The soya milk works well instead of cream. A Beaujolais or Rully goes well with this dish.

time to table - 1 hour
ingredients - to serve 6-8 people

> **2 mugs (400g) plain flour**
> **½ pack (125g) butter**
> **cup of ice cold water**
> **vegetable oil**
> **2 medium onions**
> **1 pack (200g) streaky bacon**
> **freshly-chopped parsley**
> **4 eggs**
> **2 large glasses (500ml) soya milk**
> **salt and pepper**
> **freshly-grated Parmesan cheese**

For the pastry:

1   Sift the flour into a bowl and cut up the butter into small pieces

2   Cool your hands in cold water, and blend the butter into the flour.

3   Gradually add some ice cold water, mixing in with a fork and then your hands to form a firm dough. Leave to rest in the fridge for 15-30 minutes.

4   Dust a clean work surface with flour, and roll out pastry (bigger than the size you want).

5   Roll the pastry around the rolling pin and carefully place in a buttered flan dish.

6   Move the pastry into all the crevices.

7   The pastry is best cooked blind for 20-30 minutes in a mild oven (150°C. 300°F, gas mark 2) by covering it with foil held down with clean weights or cooking granules. Check that there are no holes in the pastry otherwise the filling will leak out.

For the filling:

1   Heat the oil.

2   Finely slice the onions and cook until soft and clear. Be careful not to let them brown.

3   Remove from the heat.

4   Cut the bacon into small pieces (use lardons if in France).

5   Add some more oil and cook the bacon until it just begins to crisp up.

6   Place the onions and bacon on the pastry in the flan dish. Sprinkle with the chopped parsley.

7   Beat the eggs and mix in the soya milk thoroughly. Season with salt and pepper.

8   Pour over the filling onto the pastry, mixing in the parsley, and sprinkle with freshly-grated Parmesan cheese.

9   Cook for 30 minutes in a medium oven at 160°C (320°F, gas mark 3) or until the top is slightly brown and firm.

10   Take the quiche out of the oven, and leave to rest for 2-3 minutes when the top will settle.

Photo: see page 126

Another British favourite with a touch of French influence, and one based on a recipe that my mum used to make. Lovely for a simple family supper on a cold winter's evening.

time to table - 1½ hours
ingredients - to serve 6 people (but they will want seconds!)

6 medium sized potatoes
olive oil
2 medium sized onions
2 cloves of garlic
1kg (2 lb) good mince (lamb or beef) or minced meat left-overs
2 large carrots
1 glass of red wine
1 tin of chopped tomatoes
salt and white pepper
large knob of clarified butter
¼ mug (50ml) soya milk

1 Peel the potatoes and cut them into chunks.

2 Boil them in salted water until soft in the centre. A better way of maintaining the flavour of mashed potatoes is to steam them in a colander over boiling water.

3 Put the potatoes aside and keep warm until needed.

4 Peel and finely chop the onions. Soften them in warm olive oil in a pan.

5 Peel, débarrassé (remove the green, central germ that can be a little bitter) and finely chop the garlic. Add the garlic to the onions.

6 Add the mince and cook until all the meat is brown, turning frequently to stop it sticking.

7 Chop the carrots finely and add them to the meat.

8 Add the wine and cook for 5 minutes.

9 Add the tomatoes and mix well.

10 Season well with salt and freshly ground pepper.

11 Simmer for 45-60 minutes until the meat is tender. Turn the mixture regularly with a wooden spoon to prevent it sticking.

12 Break up the tomatoes and pour the mixture into a large deep dish.

13 Allow to cool in the fridge.

14 Mash the potatoes.

15 Add a large knob of butter and the soya milk, and season with salt and pepper.

16 Mix until the potatoes are completely smooth.

17 Use a palette knife to put the potatoes onto the meat mixture, starting with the edge. Smooth the top with a palette knife, and mark it in rows with a fork.

18 Cook for a further 15 minutes in a hot oven at 180°C (350°F, gas mark 4) until the top is nicely brown.

Serve immediately with plenty of peas. A rich, red wine, such as a Cabernet Sauvignon from Bordeaux or a Rioja goes well with this. This dish is suitable for freezing.

steak and kidney pie

A great British favourite, and based on a recipe my mother used for winter Saturday lunches, after I had been running around the school rugby pitch all morning. It can be stored frozen.

time to table - 2½ hours
ingredients - to serve 6-8 people

½kg (1lb) of braising steak
½kg (1lb) of lamb's kidney
1 large onion
vegetable oil
1 mug (200g, 6oz) plain flour
salt and pepper
1 can of lactose free beer (light or dark, depending on taste, avoid stout)
1½ large glasses (300ml) water
For the pastry:
1½ mugs (8oz) plain flour
salt
½ pack (125g) butter
cup of ice cold water
1 beaten egg

For the pie filling:
1   Cut the meat and kidneys into small chunks, removing any fat.
2   Peel and slice the onion, and soften in the oil over a mild heat. Remove and put aside.
3   Sift the flour into a dish and season with salt and pepper.
4   Roll the meat in the seasoned flour.
5   Heat some more oil in the pan and gradually add the floured meat.
6   Cook until slightly brown.
7   Add back the onions, the kidneys, and then the can of beer, allowing it to froth.
8   Pour in the water and season with more salt and pepper.
9   Cook over a gentle heat for 1-1½ hours until the meat is tender.
10 Place the mixture in a dish ready to cover with the pastry. Place an egg cup in the middle. Keep some of the sauce to serve with the pie.

For the pastry:
1   Sift the flour into a bowl and cut up the butter into small pieces.
2   Cool your hands in cold water, and blend the butter into the flour.
3   Gradually add some ice cold water, mixing in with a fork and then your hands to form a firm dough. Leave to rest in the fridge for 15-30 minutes.
4   Dust a clean work surface with flour, and roll out pastry (bigger than the size you want).
5   Wet the lip of the dish and place a thin slice of pastry around it.
6   Add the rest of the pastry on top, and trim off any extra over-lapping pastry.
7   Spike the pastry all over with a fork and cut a slit in the middle over the egg cup.
8   Brush with beaten egg and cook for 30 minutes in a medium oven (160°C, 320°F, gas mark 3) until golden brown.

These are always best cooked fresh and eaten immediately.

In this section, I start with my favourite vegetable - potatoes. There is such a wonderful variety of potatoes available now, and so many ways to cook them. It is worth finding out about these different varieties. Some are waxy and work very well in Lyonnaise or a gratin. Others are fluffy, and are best for roasting, sautéing, or in their jackets. I start to chit my potatoes in Pembrokeshire at the end of January. First 'earlies' can then be planted in February. We can then start eating them by the end of May or early June. And we will have fresh potatoes from the ground well into September.

It is quite amazing how different in taste they are when cooked immediately from the ground. Even within a few hours of digging up a first early, like Kestrel, it will have lost its sweetness and a lot of its flavour.

crispy roast potatoes

How often have you had those dreadful leathery roast potatoes in a self service restaurant or motorway service station. No more will you have to put up with this purgatory! I have found the answer. But they must be eaten at once. Even my French friends have been impressed, and asked for the recipe. Tout à fait remarkable!

time to table - 1 hour
ingredients - to serve 6-8 people

6-8 large, fluffy type potatoes
large pan of salted water
5-6 tablespoons of sunflower oil

1   Peel the potatoes, and cut them into large chunks.
2   Boil for just 5-6 minutes in salted water until the outside is soft, but the inside is still hard.
3   Drain, and put them back into the dry saucepan.
4   Replace the saucepan lid, taking care as it may still be hot.
5   Shake hard several times until the potato surfaces show fluffs on them.
6   Add the oil and shake again to coat the potatoes.
7   Place the potatoes on a flat baking tray.
8   Pour over a little more oil.
9   Roast in a hot oven at 200°C (390°F, gas mark 6) for 30-40 minutes until the potatoes are a crispy golden on the outside and soft in the middle.

If you leave the potatoes to keep warm in the oven they may lose their crispiness. So enjoy them immediately with your Sunday roast.

tony's tip:

The trick is to par boil the potatoes first, drain them off, and then shake them in the saucepan with the lid on so that the surface becomes very fluffy. This absorbs the oil during roasting and the roasties will end up beautifully crisp.
Serve with a nice glass of red Burgundy.

croquette potatoes coated in ground almonds

Almonds are very Provencal. So it was a great discovery to find how well they go with potatoes. The capers add that piquancy, making these potatoes even more special. Your guests will be wondering what the ingredients are. You can't buy this type of croquette potatoes in the supermarket! These can be stored frozen.

time to table - 1 hour
ingredients - to serve 6-8 people

8 medium sized (2kg, 4lb) potatoes
salted water
2 hard boiled eggs
2 tablespoons of capers
freshly-grated nutmeg
salt and white pepper
flour
2 eggs
1 pack (200g) ground almond
breadcrumbs
2/3 pack (200g) clarified butter

1 Peel the potatoes and boil them in salted water.
2 Drain and mash with a little butter.
3 Add the hard boiled eggs, well-chopped, the chopped capers, half the almonds and the nutmeg.
4 Mix well and season with salt and pepper.
5 Place in a fridge to cool.
6 Once the mashed potato has firmed up, take it out of the fridge and roll into logs in seasoned flour.
7 Cut the logs into slices and form into croquette shapes with your hands.
8 Brush with beaten egg and roll in ground almonds and breadcrumbs.
9 Repeat the previous stage again, to make sure the croquettes are well covered.
10 You can then place in the fridge again for I hour to firm up if you wish.
11 Fry the croquettes in butter on a medium heat, so that the butter does not burn.
12 Turn each croquette frequently and cook until nicely light brown and crisp.

Serve sprinkled with freshly-grated parsley. These are so good they can be eaten on their own as one would in Provence, perhaps with some aïoli. But they accompany well all the meat dishes described in this book.

> **tony's tip:**
>
> To ensure that the croquettes are crispy and moist on the outside, use a coating of breadcrumbs (chapulere) with the almonds after dipping each croquette in the beaten egg. And make sure you use clarified butter for frying to reduce the chance of it burning. Serve with a Provence white wine from the Mouverdre grape, or a rosé goes well with them.

gratin sans lait

So, how can you still have a gratin without milk? Here is one I use and works well with soya milk. It is therefore a modification of the classic Normandy recipe.

time to table - 45 minutes
ingredients - to serve 6-8 people

6 good sized, waxy potatoes
2 cloves of garlic
½ pack (120g) butter
salt
pepper
2 large glasses (500ml) soya milk

1 Wash and peel the potatoes.
2 Cut into thin even slices.
3 Peel and débarrassé (remove the green, central germ that can be a little bitter) the garlic.
4 Then chop finely or crush in a garlic crusher.
5 Butter a gratin dish.
6 Place a layer of sliced potatoes on the bottom of the dish.
7 Sprinkle some chopped garlic on top, and season with salt and pepper.
8 Add a few small knobs of butter.
9 Add layers until the potatoes are finished.
10 Pour the soya milk carefully over the potatoes.
11 Cook in a medium oven at 160°C (320°F, gas mark 3) for about 30 minutes until the potatoes are brown on top and soft in the middle when a knife is inserted.

Serve immediately.

---

tony's tip:

These potatoes go well with any French meat dish, such as coq au vin or fillet steak, with the appropriate wine.

I first came across Italian vegetables as a starter in a hotel restaurant in Florence. So when I got home I set about trying to make up my own recipe. I hope you will find my modifications bring out the flavour, sweetness and texture of these wonderful vegetables.

time to table - 3 hours
ingredients - to serve 6-8 people

3 courgettes
1-2 aubergines
3 peppers (red, green and yellow)
6 small tomatoes
juice and zest of 1 lemon
2 cloves of garlic
1 dessert spoon of Dijon mustard
oregano, basil and thyme
salt and pepper
1 complete bulb of garlic
3-4 tablespoons (50ml) of olive oil

1   Wash the vegetables and cut into slices after removing the seeds from inside the peppers.

2   In a large mixing bowl, add the juice and zest of the lemon, herbs, salt and pepper. Fresh herbs are best, but dried ones work fine as well.

3   Peel, débarrassé (remove the green, central germ that can be a little bitter) and finely chop the garlic, and add to the bowl.

4   Mix in the Dijon mustard. Then mix in the olive oil thoroughly.

5   Add all the chopped vegetables.

6   Turn them well by hand in the marinade, so that they are all coated.

7   Leave to marinate for 1-2 hours if possible, though they can be cooked immediately.

8   Pour the marinated vegetables onto a large flat baking tray so that they all lie as flat as possible. Add a few sprigs of fresh thyme.

9   Break up the garlic bulb into individual cloves and sprinkle over the vegetables.

10 Bake in a hot oven at 180°C (350°F, gas mark 4) for 45 minutes, until the aubergines are soft and begin to brown.

11 Arrange the vegetables on a serving plate. Season with salt and pepper.

12 Drizzle a little olive oil over them.

Serve immediately as a starter or with a meat main course.

tony's tip:

These taste beautiful after cooking simply on a skillet with a little olive oil without the marinade. But, if oven roasting, add the garlic last, 10-15 minutes before the end, otherwise the cloves will burn. Serve with a chilled, dry Italian white wine, such as a Frascati.

mashed carrot and coriander

Coriander complements the sweetness of carrots so well. Use fresh leaves if you can. Most supermarkets sell the plants in small pots. I like to serve this dish in individual ramekins. They are so tasty simply on their own with a knob of butter.

time to table - 30 minutes
ingredients - to serve 6-8 people

8 (1kg, 2lb) large carrots
1 tablespoon of ground coriander
4 tablespoons of chopped fresh coriander leaves
salt
pepper
butter

1 Peel and roughly chop the carrots.
2 Soften by steaming over boiling water for about 15 minutes.
3 Drain and mash to a pulp.
4 Add the ground coriander, salt and pepper, and finally the chopped fresh coriander leaves.
5 Butter 6-8 small moulds or ramekins.
6 Spoon the carrot mix into them.
7 Leave until required.
8 Warm in a mild oven after covering with foil.

To serve, turn the ramekins upside down on individual plates or a serving plate. Garnish with freshly-chopped coriander leaves.

tony's tip:

Try and get fresh coriander. It makes such a difference to the wonderful aroma and flavour of this dish.

When I found my family had to give up milk, it put a temporary end to the gratin potatoes that we all liked so much. Then I rediscovered butter and onions. These combine to make this potato dish both moist and sweet. It is now one of my firm favourites, accompanying any kind of kind of hot or cold meat, quiche, or even salmon. It has a crispy light brown top that always looks so appetising.

time to table - 45 minutes
ingredients - to serve 8 people

6 large (2kg, 4lb) waxy potatoes
3 medium onions (French if possible, with those lovely purple streaks)
2/3 pack (200g) of clarified butter
salt and pepper
Parmesan cheese
parsley

1   Peel the potatoes and store under water until required.
2   For once we are not going to finely chop the onions. Rather, cut them in half, peel them, and slice into thin half rings.
3   Melt half the butter in a pan over a medium heat.
4   Cook the onions until soft and slightly yellow, but not brown.
5   Remove and put aside.
6   Drain the potatoes and dry them on kitchen paper.
7   Cut the potatoes into slices about 1-2cm thick. A key to this dish is to have all the slices the same thickness.
8   Melt the rest of the butter in the pan and gradually add the potato slices in batches.
9   Turn the slices until they are all coated with the melted butter.
10   Add the cooked onions and mix them in thoroughly.
11   Season well with salt and pepper. Then pour the mixture into a large gratin dish.
12   Sprinkle with freshly-grated Parmesan, if you are allowed a little cheese.
13   Bake in the oven at 180°C (350°F, gas mark 4) for about 30 minutes, until the potatoes are soft but still firm, and the top is a golden brown.

Sprinkle with freshly-chopped parsley and serve. These potatoes can accompany any meat dish beautifully. You can enjoy them on their own, or why not have them with a little aïoli.

Photo: see page 127

---

tony's tip:

Remember to use clarified butter to prevent burning. Sprinkling the dish with a little freshly-chopped parsley just before serving increases its mouth-watering appearance. Delicious with a Provence rosé or Beaujolais before the meat course.

roast mixed vegetables

This is a great way to do a mixture of vegetables to eat with any roast meat. It is how I discovered the wonders of roast garlic. The cloves from at least one whole bulb will be added to my mixed vegetables. The result is that the children spend half an hour at lunch searching for those now succulent, sweetly cooked cloves hidden by the rest of the delicious vegetables.

time to table - 1 hour
ingredients - to serve 6-8 people

8 carrots
8 parsnips
½ swede
4 onions
6 peppers (red, green and yellow)
1 complete bulb of garlic
6 medium sized potatoes
rosemary
thyme
salt and pepper
½ mug (100 ml) olive oil

1   Peel the carrots, parsnips and swede, and chop into chunks.
2   Peel and quarter the onions.
3   Remove the tops from the peppers, the seeds and the white bits inside, and discard.
4   Cut into chunks.
5   Peel 3 cloves of garlic, débarrassé (remove the green, central germ that can be a little bitter) and chop finely.
6   Keep the rest of the garlic in their skins.
7   Wash and peel the potatoes, and chop into chunks.
8   Place all the vegetables in a large mixing bowl.
9   Add the chopped herbs, salt and pepper.
10 Turn them with your hands.
11 Then add the olive oil and turn again until all the vegetables are well covered.
12 Place in 1-2 large baking trays.
13 Bake in a hot oven at 180°C (350°F gas mark 4) for 45 minutes until tender and beginning to brown.

Serve immediately. These go well with any roast meat, such as beef, lamb or pork.

> **tony's tip:**
> The sweetness of the centre of the garlic cloves is just unbelievable if you haven't tried them before. I usually have to put two bulbs of garlic in for my family!
> Drink a wine appropriate for the meat.

This recipe is ideal if you are in a hurry and still want those crispy, roast potatoes. No peeling or pre-cooking is needed. Just slice them up and mix with the marinade. Make sure you use a large roasting pan, as the potatoes benefit from plenty of space.

time to table - 45 minutes
ingredients - to serve 6-8 people

8 medium sized potatoes
1 onion
2 cloves of garlic
salt
pepper
2-3 tablespoons of olive oil
sprig of thyme
parsley

1 Wash and dry the potatoes, but do not peel them.
2 Cut into thin slices and place them in a bowl.
3 Peel and slice the onions into rings.
4 Peel the garlic and chop finely.
5 Add the garlic and onions to the potatoes.
6 Season with salt and pepper.
7 Add some thyme leaves.
8 Pour in the olive oil.
9 Turn the mix with your hands to cover the potatoes.
10 Lay out the potatoes on a flat baking tray.
11 Add 2-3 springs of thyme.
12 Cook in a hot oven at about 175°C (345°F, gas mark 4) for 40 minutes, or until golden brown.

Serve immediately, garnished with chopped parsley.

---

tony's tip:

These potatoes are lovely on their own, or with a strong fish or meat dish. Drink a wine which complements the fish or meat.

stir-fry vegetables

These crispy vegetable are beautiful on their own as a light veggie lunch, with maybe a slice of Italian bread such as Ciabatta, provided you make sure it is lactose free. Alternatively, they go well with most of the chicken or pork dishes recipes described in this book. The leek and the daffodil are the emblems of Wales. Don't try eating daffodils. They are highly poisonous! But leeks have a beautiful sweetness and succulent texture. You can add courgettes as well, but I find that they tend to add a touch of bitterness. So I usually keep to the three types of vegetables I have used here.

time to table - 15 minutes
ingredients - to serve 6 people

3 carrots
3 leeks
2 red peppers
2 yellow peppers
2 green pepper
2 cloves of garlic
4 tablespoons of olive oil
salt
pepper

1   Peel the carrots and slice lengthwise very thinly.
2   Cut the ends off the leeks, wash them carefully to remove any earth trapped within, and remove the outer layer.
3   Cut the leeks in half and slice lengthwise very thinly.
4   Cut the heads off the peppers and remove the seeds. Cut into thin slices.
5   Peel and débarrassé (remove the green, central germ that can be a little bitter) the garlic.
6   Chop finely.
7   Heat some olive oil in a large pan.
8   Add the carrots, leeks and peppers.
9   Cook for 2-3 minutes and add the garlic.
10 Turn a few times using cooking tongs.
11 Season with salt and freshly-ground black pepper.

Serve immediately, while still slightly crunchy. They go very well with stir-fry chicken for a light lunch.

Photo: see page 128

---

tony's tip:

Make sure you only cook these fabulous vegetables for a few minutes, so that the sweetness of the leeks blends with the crispness of the carrots and peppers.
Serve with a dry, well-chilled Italian white wine, such as a Frascati.

Potatoes in their jackets are always a simple way of cooking potatoes. I like my skins crispy. So I coat them in a little olive oil and season them before roasting. Otherwise just dry them well and cook them. Once they are crispy, eat them immediately. If you want to keep them aside, the skins will probably turn soft. But, if you return them to a hot oven for a few more minutes they will crisp up again. This recipe shows how you can stuff them with a variety of fillings.

time to table - 1½ hours
ingredients - to serve 4-6 people (at least 3 potato halves each)

6-8 good sized potatoes
olive oil
6 slices of streaky bacon
2 medium onions
2/3 pack (200g) butter
6 mushrooms
Dijon mustard
salt and pepper
1/3 cup of soya milk
Parmesan or gruyère cheese

1   Wash and dry the potatoes. Brush with olive oil and sprinkle with a little salt.
2   Bake in a hot oven at 180°C (350°F, gas mark 4) for 45 minutes.
3   Remove from the oven and allow to cool.
4   Chop the bacon into small pieces and cook in the oven until crispy.
5   Peel and finely chop the onions. Cook in a knob of butter until soft and yellow.
6   Clean the mushrooms with dry kitchen paper. Do not wash with water.
7   Slice the mushrooms and cook in a knob of butter for just 2-3 minutes.
8   Once the potatoes are cool, cut each in half and spoon out the inside into a mixing bowl.
9   Place the empty skins on a baking dish.
10 Add a knob of butter or a dash of olive oil to the inside of each skin.
11 Mash the inside of the potatoes, and mix well with some butter, salt, pepper, and then the soya milk.
12 Put 1/3 of the mashed potatoes into a separate bowl.
13 Add the cooked bacon and a little Dijon mustard.
14 Spoon this mixture into 1/3 of the potato skins.
15 Now take another 1/3 of the mashed potatoes and mix with the softened onions.
16 Spoon this into another 1/3 of the potato skins.
17 Mix the final 1/3 of the mashed potatoes with the sliced mushrooms.
18 Spoon this into the last 1/3 of the potato skins.
19 Sprinkle the stuffed potatoes with grated cheese if you are allowed this.
20 Bake in a medium to hot oven at 170°C (340°F, gas mark 3-4) for 30 minutes.
21 The skins should be crispy, and the tops brown with melted cheese.

Serve immediately on their own, or with a little salad and dry white wine, such as a Chardonnay.

stuffed peppers

Using a mix of different coloured peppers makes this dish very attractive to serve. The sweet crunchiness of the peppers blends beautifully with the softness of the rice inside.

time to table - 1 hour
ingredients - to serve 4 people (2 peppers each)

8 medium sized peppers (mix of red, green and yellow)
olive oil
2 cloves of garlic
2 medium onions
1 mug (200g) long grain rice
6 slices of streaky bacon
basil
oregano
½ mug of dry Italian white wine
1 chicken stock cube
1 mug (200ml) water

1 Wash and then dry the peppers.
2 Cut the tops off and retain.
3 Remove the seeds and white bits inside, and drizzle in a little olive oil.
4 Chop the bacon into small pieces.
5 Peel and finely chop the onions and garlic.
6 Soften in hot olive oil in a flat pan.
7 Then add the bacon and cook for 5-10 minutes until soft.
8 Add the rice and turn until the rice is well coated.
9 Add the herbs and white wine.
10 Dissolve the stock cube in the water and add to the rice. Season with salt and pepper.
11 Place the lid on the pan and cook until the rice has absorbed the liquid. Add more water if necessary.
12 Allow to cool for 5 minutes.
13 Spoon the rice mix into the pepper shells, pressing down until the rice is to the top.
14 Drizzle on a little olive oil, and place the tops back on.
15 Cook for 30 minutes in a medium oven at 160°C (320°F, gas mark 3).

Serve immediately with a watercress salad.

---

tony's tip:

Place the tops of the peppers back on about 10 minutes before the end. This adds to the attraction of the dish and ensures the tops will have a crunchiness to contrast with the rest of the pepper.
Serve with a light, red wine, such as a Beaujolais or a soft Chilean Merlot.

A little salsa adds so much to many dishes. It is an ideal complement with quiche, for example. The trick is to remove both the skin and the seeds from the tomatoes. This increases their sweetness.

time to table - 15 minutes
ingredients - to serve 6 people

6 ripe Italian tomatoes
1 clove of garlic
3 spring onions
fresh basil
salt
pepper
4 tablespoons of olive oil
1 teaspoon of white wine vinegar
juice of 1 lime
½ teaspoon of caster sugar

1   Make a cross on the top of the tomatoes, and soak them in boiling water for 5 minutes.
2   Using a slotted spoon place them in ice cold water for 5 minutes.
3   Remove from the water and the skins will now slip off easily.
4   Cut the tomatoes into quarters and remove the seeds and watery centre.
5   Chop finely and place in a small serving bowl.
6   Peel and débarrassé (remove the green, central germ that can be a little bitter) the garlic, and add to the tomatoes.
7   Remove the roots and outer layer of leaves from the spring onions.
8   Chop into small pieces and add to the tomatoes.
9   Add chopped basil and season well with salt and pepper.
10 Mix in the olive oil, and then a little wine vinegar and the lime juice.
11 Finally add the sugar to bring out the sweetness of the tomatoes.

This will keep, covered in the fridge, for several days. Serve with some of the spicy meat starters in the Entrée section or a quiche.

tony's tip:

It is essential to remove all of the seeds and insides of the tomatoes, so that the dish is sweet and moist, but not too watery.

turmeric rice

If you want a more interesting rice than just plain, then this is the recipe for you. The turmeric gives it a special flavour and a marvellous yellow colour. This rice adds something special to oriental dishes.

time to table - 40 minutes
ingredients - to serve 6 people

vegetable oil
1 dessert spoon of turmeric
1 dessert spoon of cumin
1 onion
2 mugs (400g) white, long grain rice
salt
pepper
2-3 large glasses (500-750ml) water

1 Heat 2-3 tablespoons of oil in a large, flat pan.
2 Add the turmeric and cumin, and fry for 2 minutes.
3 Peel and finely chop the onion.
4 Add to the spices.
5 Cook the onion over a mild heat until soft and clear, but not brown.
6 Add the rice and turn it so that the mixture is well covered.
7 Cook the rice for 2-3 minutes.
8 Season with salt and pepper.
9 Add water gradually
10 Cook until the rice is 'al dente'. Add more water If necessary.
11 Check the seasoning to taste.

Serve with a curry, spicy chicken or even sweet and sour pork.

Photo: see page 124

tony's tip:

When using Asian spices, it is always worthwhile frying them for a couple of minutes. This brings out the oils that make them so aromatic and flavoursome.

All salads must be made fresh. They can be kept in the fridge for a few hours, but cannot be frozen. The sauces and vinaigrettes can be stored in the fridge for days or even weeks. Add them just before serving to ensure that the salad remains as crisp as possible.

Some of my salads can be found in the Entrée section.

fennel and radish salad

Real Italian prosciutto ham makes this dish special. But, if you can't get it, use streaky bacon or French lardons. These will still make a really nice and unusual salad. I like to grow my own radishes. It was a revelation when I discovered you can eat the leaves as well as the red bulbs.

time to table - 10 minutes
ingredients - to serve 6-8 people

½ pack (100g) streaky bacon or prosciutto ham
1 whole fennel
1 bunch of radishes
juice of 1 lemon
salt
pepper
Parmesan cheese
olive oil

1 Cut the bacon or ham into small pieces.
2 Bake in a hot oven at 180°C (350°F, gas mark 4) for 10 minutes until crisp.
3 Put aside.
4 Wash the fennel and radishes.
5 Cut off the tails and most of the leaves from the radishes but leave the top 2 cm.
6 Cut into fine slices and place on a flat salad plate.
7 Season with salt and pepper.
8 Chop the fennel into chunks and place them on top of the radishes.
9 Season with salt and pepper.
10 Sprinkle the lemon juice and the crispy bacon or ham pieces over the radishes.
11 Add a few slivers of Parmesan cheese using a vegetable peeler, if you are allowed this.
12 Then drizzle with olive oil.

Serve immediately.

---

tony's tip:

Always leave the lemon juice and olive oil until just before serving, so that the radish and fennel remains crisp.
Serve with a chilled French white wine, such as a Sancerre.

You can't have a salad without a vinaigrette. The problem I have found is that so many are either too bland or too sharp, even when using the vinegar as sparingly as possible. The answer is to add a little sweetness, for example using some honey. Alternatively, using lemon juice results in much less sharpness than with vinegar. See what you think. I am repeating this honey vinaigrette recipe for completeness. Take care not to add too much honey.

time to table - 5 minutes
ingredients - to serve 6 people

juice and zest of 1 lemon
juice and zest of 1 lime
1 dessert spoon of Dijon mustard
1 tablespoon of honey
salt
pepper
1 clove of garlic
8 tablespoons of olive oil
clarified butter

1   Pour the juice and zest of the lemon and lime into a bowl.
2   Add the Dijon mustard, honey, salt and pepper.
3   Mix with a fork or small whisk.
4   Débarrassé (remove the green, central germ that can be a little bitter) the garlic, and chop it very finely. It is particularly important to do this when eating garlic raw.
5   Add the chopped garlic to the mixture.
6   Pour in the olive oil slowly, mixing with a fork or whisk until it forms a firm emulsion.
7   Pour into a small jug and cool until required.
8   Sprinkle some warm clarified butter onto the salad after the vinaigrette.

155

tony's tip:

As I suggested earlier, a trick is to sprinkle a little warm clarified butter over the salad just after the vinaigrette. And make sure the vinaigrette still retains some sharpness.

saffron vinaigrette

Saffron has an incredible colour and flavour. It is expensive. But the proper stuff sold in small jars is what you need for this recipe.

time to table - 30 minutes
ingredients - to serve 6 people

2 tablespoons of white wine vinegar
2 teaspoons of caster sugar
saffron
salt
pepper
olive oil

1 Warm the vinegar on a mild heat.
2 Add the sugar and salt and allow it to dissolve.
3 Mix in the saffron.
4 Cool.
5 Season with salt and pepper.
6 Mix with 3 times the volume of olive oil.
7 Store in a sealed jar until needed.

tony's tip:
Always try and buy the real McCoy. Expensive, but worth it.

So many restaurant desserts contain milk or cream. Here you will find all these delicious desserts are lactose free.

Some of these dishes can be stored frozen.

apple and almond tarts

These are delicious with a cup of tea, or after a meal with coffee. For the pate sucré - see the later recipe for tarte tartin.

time to table - 30 minutes
ingredients - to serve 6-8 people

3 dessert apples
2/3 pack (150g) unsalted butter
8 tablespoons of caster sugar
splash of Calvados
4 egg yolks
½ mug (100g) ground almonds
3 tablespoons of plain flour

1   Peel, quarter and core the apples.
2   Cut each quarter further in half.
3   Melt a knob of butter over a mild heat in a pan.
4   Add 4 tablespoons of sugar and then the apples. Cook until the sugar begins to caramelise.
5   Add the Calvados.
6   Cook for just 1-2 minutes more, and put aside to cool.
7   Roll out the pate sucré pastry when ready, and cut it into rounds so that they fit into 6-8 small, buttered metal flan dishes.
8   Trim off the edges and fork the bottoms well.
9   Cook 'blind' for 20 minutes in a medium oven 160°C (320°F, gas mark 3) if you wish.
10 Put the rest of the butter in a mixing bowl and fork well until creamy.
11 Mix in thoroughly 4 tablespoons of sugar.
12 Then mix in thoroughly the egg yolks.
13 Mix in the almonds and flour.
14 Place a small cluster of the apple mix in the centre of each pastried flan dish.
15 Spoon the almond mix around the apples.
16 Bake in a medium oven at 160°C (320°F, gas mark 3) for 20 minutes until the almond mix begins to brown.
17 Remove from the oven and allow to cool.
18 Take the tarts carefully out of each flan dish.
19 Arrange on a serving plate.

Serve cold or slightly warm.

tony's tip:

These can be stored for several days in a tight biscuit tin. But keep them on their own, so that they stay nice and fresh. Serve with a small glass of Amaretto, or even a nice cup of afternoon tea, with soya milk of course.

Now this is a real British pudding, with a lovely gooey topping, best served piping hot. In this recipe, I find that the good old British Bramley makes the best apple crumble.

time to table - 40 minutes
ingredients - to serve 6-8 people

6-8 Bramley apples (cooking apples)
½ pack (150g) unsalted butter
1 mug (200g, 6oz) plain flour
6 tablespoons of granulated sugar
3 tablespoons (50ml) of Calvados
1½ mugs (300g, 10oz) caster sugar
nutmeg
2 tablespoons of brown sugar

1   Peel and quarter the apples.
2   Remove the cores.
3   Keep them in water with a slice of lemon to prevent them going brown.
4   Sift the flour into a mixing bowl.
5   Add the butter, chopped, and feel it into the flour with your hands.
6   Add the sugar and keep mixing it with your hands until it forms a crumb-like mix.
7   Drain the apples and place them in an oven-proof dish. Sprinkle with 4-6 tablespoons of sugar.
8   Put the crumble on top of the apple mix and sprinkle with a little brown sugar and fresh nutmeg.
9   Cook in a medium oven at 160°C (320°F, gas mark 3) for 30 minutes.

Delicious served with lactose free custard.

tony's tip:

Don't cook the Bramleys first. This allows them to stay firm.
Why not try a small glass of Calvar or Muscat with it?

apple flapjack

I love flapjack. So this is a tea time favourite. But when I found the canteen in work selling various fruit flapjacks containing added milk powder, and not very tasty anyway, I thought why not use some of the apples from the garden. The result is a classic flapjack taste and texture, as you bite into each slice. Then you get a surprise, as you discover the soft, gooey apple centre.

time to table - 45 minutes
ingredients - to serve 6-8 people

1 pack (250g) unsalted butter
6 dessert apples (from the garden, if possible)
6 tablespoons of granulated or brown sugar
3 tablespoons of honey or golden syrup
juice of ½ lemon
1 teaspoon of ground cinnamon
pinch of ground cloves
2 mugs (400g, 10oz) oatmeal

1 Melt 100g butter in a pan.
2 Peel and core the apples.
3 Slice and add to the melted butter.
4 Add 2 tablespoons of sugar.
5 Mix well and add the honey.
6 Add a little Calvados if you like!
7 Add the juice of ½ lemon.
8 Mix in the spices and put aside after 5 minutes more cooking. Make sure the apples keep their firmness and do not go into a pulp.
9 Melt the rest of the butter (150g) in another pan.
10 Add 4 tablespoons of sugar and then the oatmeal.
11 Place half the flapjack mix on a buttered flat baking tray.
12 Flatten well.
13 Cover with the apple mix.
14 Then add the rest of the flapjack, pressing it down hard.
15 Cook in a medium oven at 160°C (320°F, gas mark 3) for 30 minutes. It still needs to be slightly soft. If you cook it too long, the flapjack becomes too crunchy.
16 Remove and allow to cool a little for 10 minutes.

Cut the apple flapjack into squares and enjoy with a nice cup of afternoon tea.

---

tony's tip:

These will store for several days, on their own, in a tight biscuit tin, if you are lucky and they have not been eaten first!

Tuiles are a classic French biscuit. But many biscuits can have added lactose. Here is an idea I had when you can't have biscuits with ice cream, and they are lactose free. They can be eaten as a dessert or with a cup of tea. Try taking some into work for elevenses. They will really impress your colleagues.

time to table - 1 hour
ingredients - to serve 6 people (with one tuile each)

For the tuiles:
1/3 pack (100g) unsalted butter, clarified
4 dessert spoons of icing sugar
2 egg whites
2 dessert spoons of ground almonds
For the apple filling:
3 dessert apples
1/3 pack (100g) unsalted butter
4 dessert spoons of sugar
dash of cinnamon
splash of Calvados

1 Soften the butter in a warm bowl and beat it with a fork until creamy.
2 Add the icing sugar and beat again well.
3 Mix in the egg whites.
4 Using a dessert spoon place spoonfuls of the mix on a buttered baking tray.
5 Bake for about 20 minutes in a medium oven at 160°C (320°F, gas mark 3) until the edges are beginning to brown.
6 Remove from the oven and allow to cool for 15 minutes.
7 Using a cake slice, place the tuiles on a serving plate.
8 While the tuiles are cooking, peel the apples, quarter and remove the cores.
9 Melt the butter in a large pan and add the sugar.
10 When it begins to caramelise add the sliced apples.
11 Add a dash of cinnamon and a splash of Calvados.
12 Cook for just a few minutes making sure the apples remain firm.
13 Spoon the apple mix onto the tuiles.

Serve warm immediately.

tony's tip:

Tuiles go well with the lemon sorbet - see recipe later in the book, p166.
Serve with a nice cup of afternoon tea, or at dinner with a small glass of Calvar or Amaretto.

chocolate mousse

Mousse au chocolate - ah, magnifique! Vive La France! You can't live without chocolate. But chocolate mousse recipes often use cream, and milk chocolate and some dark chocolate contain milk and added lactose. But this recipe book shows you how to enjoy chocolate again without being ill. I have found you can leave out the cream. So here is my method. To make sure it really is lactose free I use dark chocolate labelled 70% cocoa. Don't worry too much if it says on the packet 'may contain some traces of milk'. This probably means that it has been made in a vessel that had some milk in it at some time. It may be a problem if you are allergic to milk proteins. But it is unlikely that there will be enough lactose to cause a problem if you are lactose intolerant.

time to table - 2 hours
ingredients - to serve 6-8 people

5 eggs, separated
1½ bars (200g) genuine dark chocolate (70% cocoa)
zest and juice of 1 lime
2 dessert spoons of caster sugar
2 tablespoons of cognac or rum

1 Beat all the egg whites in a large bowl to form soft peaks.
2 Put aside.
3 Beat the egg yolks with the sugar.
4 Add the zest and lime juice, and a little cognac or rum if you like.
5 Melt the chocolate in a bain-marie, or a small bowl over simmering water.
6 Pour the chocolate mix into the beaten egg yolk mixture.
7 Then add the beaten egg whites, and fold in very carefully.
8 Cool in the fridge for 1-2 hours before serving.

Serve chilled with a small glass of brandy or rum.

---

tony's tip:

Always melt chocolate in a bowl over boiling water without letting the bowl touch the water. Do not melt the chocolate directly over heat or in boiling water. This will ruin it.

chocolate torte sans crème

This recipe is so delicious and appetising that there is never much left after the first sitting! This can be stored frozen.

time to table - 30 minutes
ingredients - to serve 6 people (if you are lucky!)

2½ bars (250g) genuine dark chocolate (70% cocoa)
4 eggs, separated
4 tablespoons of caster sugar
1 dessert spoon of plain flour
icing sugar
For adults:
the zest and juice of 1 lime
2-3 dessert spoons of dark rum

1 Melt the chocolate in a bain-marie.
2 Separate the eggs.
3 Whisk the yolks with the sugar.
4 Add the zest and juice of the lime and rum if you wish. Children usually prefer it without these.
5 Add the melted chocolate and stir well.
6 Add the spoonful of flour to keep the torte firm when cooked.
7 Whisk the egg whites to a soft peak.
8 Carefully fold the chocolate mixture into the egg whites.
9 Pour the mix into a buttered cake tin.
10 Add a few broken pieces of chocolate into the mix.
11 Bake in a medium oven at 160°C (320°F, gas mark 3) for 15-20 minutes until firm on top. The centre should still be a bit runny.
12 Cool if you wish.
13 Use a knife to clear the torte from the edge of the tin.
14 Place a serving plate on top, and invert so that the torte drops onto the dish.
15 Carefully, with a flat knife, slice under the torte and ease it off the bottom of the cake tin.
16 Sprinkle with icing sugar or cocoa through a sieve before serving.

Photo: see page 129

tony's tip:
Lovely served warm or cold with a small glass of dark rum at the end of a meal.

chocolate truffles

These are gobbled up by my family after dinner. They have a crisp, sugary outside with a rich, soft chocolate centre. Yummy! Try them with a small glass of rum.

time to table - 1½ hours
ingredients - to serve 6-8 people (if you are lucky!)

2 bars (250g) genuine dark chocolate (70% cocoa)
2 egg yolks
4 dessert spoons of caster sugar
¼ mug (50ml) of dark rum
icing sugar

1   Melt the chocolate in a bain-marie until completely smooth.
2   Whisk the egg yolks with the sugar in a bowl.
3   Add the rum.
4   Add the melted chocolate and mix until smooth.
5   Leave in a fridge for 30-60 minutes until the chocolate mixture is firm.
6   Place some icing sugar in a dish and dust your hands with some.
7   Put a dessert spoon of the chocolate mixture into the icing sugar.
8   Then roll each spoonful into a small ball.
9   Coat again with icing sugar and place on a serving plate.
10 Keep covered at room temperature, or for longer periods in the fridge.

Serve with an espresso coffee.

tony's tip:
This recipe makes about 15 decent-sized truffles. But beware! They will disappear before you can blink twice!
They are delicious with a small glass of rum.

This is one of my standard desserts when I am entertaining a big party. But get some help. It is quite time-consuming processing all the different fruits. You can add a liqueur, but this not really necessary.

time to table - 2 hours
ingredients - to serve a good-sized party

> **1 mug (200ml) water**
> **juice and zest of 1 lemon**
> **4 dessert spoons of granulated sugar**
> **fresh fruit - peaches, oranges, pears, apples, grapes, kiwi fruit, strawberries, raspberries, a pineapple, nectarines, bananas**

1 Put the water in a saucepan and dissolve the sugar on a mild heat.
2 Add the lemon juice and zest, taking care to remove all the pips first.
3 Bring to the boil and simmer for 5 minutes. Put aside to cool.
4 Boil a kettle. Place the peaches in a bowl and pour the boiling water over the top.
5 Leave for 5 minutes.
6 With a slotted spoon remove the peaches and put them in cold water.
7 The skins should then slip off.
8 Quarter the peaches and remove the stone. Add to the fruit salad bowl in slices.
9 Cut the peel off the oranges. Cut into quarters from the top.
10 Then with a sharp knife cut the edges off each segment.
11 Place the segments and juice in the serving bowl.
12 Peel the pears. Quarter and remove the core. Cut into segments and add to the oranges.
13 Wash and then quarter the apples, and remove the cores.
14 Cut into small pieces and add to the rest of the fruit in the bowl.
15 Quarter the nectarines and remove the stone. Slice and add to the fruit salad.
16 Peel and slice the pineapple into chunks, and add it to the fruit salad.
17 Wash the grapes and cut into halves. Add into the bowl.
18 Peel the kiwi fruit, cut into pieces and add into the bowl.
19 Add other fruit such as strawberries and raspberries for more colour and taste, if available.
20 Pour the lemon juice onto the fruit, cover and leave in the fridge of 1-2 hours.
21 When ready to serve, peel and cut the bananas into thin slices. Only add to the rest of the fruit just before serving, otherwise the banana tends to brown.
22 Putting a little Kirsch in adds a little extra before serving.

This classic fruit salad needs no cream. The key to the recipe is the lemon juice. And use unwaxed lemons. Boil the juice to kill any natural yeast, otherwise in a day or so the fruit salad will start bubbling as it ferments!

Try it with a small glass of Muscat from Provence. Delicious!

lemon sorbet

This is such a simple dessert, and so refreshing. Lemon sorbet is lovely as an alternative to ice cream. But also a sorbet is very nice as a palette cleanser after a fish entrée, before the meat course. In which case don't drink any more wine until you have tasted the meat. Make enough sorbet, as your family or guests are likely to want seconds! Take care if you have a sorbet in a restaurant. Check that it really is just water-ice, and that there has been no added milk or cream.

time to table - 2 hours
ingredients - to serve 6 people

zest and juice of 4 lemons
1 mug (200ml) granulated sugar
water

1   Put the lemon juice and zest into a mug and top it up with water.
2   Put this into a small saucepan and add the sugar.
3   Heat until the sugar is dissolved. Simmer for 5 minutes.
4   Allow to cool for 10 minutes.
5   Pour through a sieve into a bowl and place in the freezer.
6   Every hour whisk thoroughly to break up the ice crystals.
7   Continue this until frozen.

Remove the sorbet from the freezer 15 minutes before needed.

Photo: see page 130

---

tony's tip:

Take care not to boil off too much water, otherwise the sorbet won't freeze properly. If the sorbet won't freeze, whisk in a little water. Use a spoon or ice cream server warmed slightly in hot water to spoon the sorbet into glasses.
It is best eaten without wine. But the almond tuiles are a very nice accompaniment.

This is simply a delightfully light and refreshing dessert after a heavy meal, with a hint of cognac.

time to table - 1½ hours
ingredients - to serve 6 people

4 big, juicy oranges
2-3 mugs (400-600ml) water
juice of 1 lemon
6 tablespoons of granulated sugar
2 tablespoons of a good cognac

1   Cut the tops and bottoms off the oranges.
2   Remove all the peel.
3   Cut the oranges into 1cm thick slices, and remove the central pith and any pips.
4   Arrange the slices in a serving dish.
5   Meanwhile put the water and sugar in a saucepan, add the lemon juice and cut up skin of 1-2 oranges.
6   Boil, and then simmer for 10 minutes to reduce the juice by one third.
7   Allow this to cool for 5 minutes, and then pour the juice through a sieve over the orange slices.
8   Add a splash of the cognac, or even more if you dare!
9   Chill in the fridge for an hour or so before serving.

Serve 2-3 segments per person.

Photo: see page 131

167

---

tony's tip:

To remove the peel use a small, sharp knife to cut around the orange in a circular motion, taking away all the skin and pith and leaving the flesh of the orange naked and beautifully juicy.
This dish needs no cream, but a small glass of cognac would not go amiss.

peaches italienne

I discovered this dish while at a beach café in the south of Tuscany on a really hot August day while on holiday with Italian friends. It seemed so simple, and it is really refreshing after a pasta main course.

time to table - 2 hours
ingredients - to serve 6 people (one peach each)

6 ripe peaches, or enough for one per person
6 dessert spoons of caster sugar
1 bottle of Italian white wine
2 cinnamon sticks
¼ mug (50ml) Amaretto
fresh mint

1 Wash the peaches and place them in a shallow casserole dish.
2 Sprinkle with sugar and add the wine.
3 Add the cinnamon.
4 Bring to the boil, cover and simmer for 30 minutes.
5 Remove from the heat, and dip the peaches immediately in ice cold water. The skins should then slip off.
6 Discard the cinnamon, but retain the beautifully coloured juice.
7 Cool in the fridge.
8 Place the peaches in a serving dish and pour over the sauce.
9 Check for sweetness.
10 Add the Amaretto and chill well before serving.

This dish is so lush it just does not need any cream. Serve with a leaf of mint on each peach.

tony's tip:

It is vital that the peaches are ripe. Cut a little cross in the top of the peach to allow the skin to be peeled off easily after being immersed in cold water.
A glass of dessert wine, such as a Sauterne or Muscat, well-chilled, is nice with this. Or simply enjoy a small glass of Amaretto.

Liqueurs always make a dessert special. Calvados with apple, Amaretto with almonds, rum with chocolate, and Cointreau with strawberries. But what on earth goes with pineapple? While experimenting, I found that Kirsch goes really well. This is not in any way a heavy dessert. Just right after the preceding six courses!

time to table - 2 hours
ingredients - to serve 6 people

1 fresh, juicy pineapple
½ mug (100ml) Kirsch
4-5 tablespoons of icing sugar
3-4 leaves of fresh mint

1   Cut the top and bottom off the pineapple.
2   Then cut off the skin. Professional cooks know that the spikes on the outside of a pineapple are arranged in a helix, and this can be used to remove the skin more efficiently.
3   Place the pineapple on a chopping board and carefully cut vertically around the central core which is hard and unpalatable.
4   Cut the four long slices into small pieces and place in a flat serving dish.
5   Pour the Kirsch over the top.
6   Then sprinkle with the icing sugar through a sieve.
7   Place the fresh mint leaves on top and cover.
8   Leave to cool in the fridge for 1-2 hours.

Serve on its own, or with a small glass of Kirsch.

---

tony's tip:

Make sure you cut out the central core of the pineapple. This is hard and chewy. Removing it leaves just the soft, succulent parts of the fruit.

summer pudding

My family just love this in June and July. The pudding can be stored frozen, kept in its preparation dish.

time to table - 3 hours
ingredients - to serve 6-8 people

1 punnet, or tin, each of: rhubarb, strawberries, raspberries, blackcurrants, red currants, blackberries and gooseberries
4 tablespoons of granulated sugar
water
1 loaf of home made, lactose free bread (stale)

1 Clean the fruit.
2 Chop the rhubarb and place it in a large saucepan.
3 Add the sugar and just enough water to prevent the fruit sticking.
4 Heat until boiling and simmer with the lid on for 5-10 minutes.
5 Add the rest of the fruit and simmer for a further 10 minutes. Do not allow the fruit to go into a mush.
6 Separate the juice from the fruit by passing the liquid through a sieve. Keep both the fruit and the juice.
7 Cut the bread into medium thick slices. Trim off the crusts.
8 Dip each slice in the juice and place them around the inside of a mixing bowl, with one slice on the bottom first.
9 Pour the fruit into the centre of the bowl lined with the bread.
10 Top with the last slice of bread soaked in the fruit juice.
11 Keep the rest of the juice aside in a small jug.
12 Seal the top with a small plate, and place a heavy weight on top.
13 Allow to set in the fridge for at least 2-3 hours, or even overnight.
14 Remove the weight and plate.
15 Gently slip a flat knife around the edge of the bread lining the bowl.
16 Place a serving plate on top. Turn upside down, holding the serving plate firmly against the bowl.
17 Tap the bottom of the bowl. The summer pudding should drop onto the serving plate.
18 Remove the bowl to reveal the beautifully coloured summer pudding.
19 Store covered in the fridge until needed.

Serve slices topped with a little of the remaining fruit juice. No cream or extra sugar should be needed. A glass of port will not go amiss with this wonderfully coloured dessert.

This famous British dessert works in winter using tinned fruit. But is transformed using fresh fruit you can buy in the supermarket at any time of year. My aim each summer is make at least one summer pudding entirely using fruit from my garden.

This is a recipe I used for my wedding feast 20 years ago. Stephanie and I picked a large basket of strawberries that morning, simply sprinkled sugar over them and then poured a whole bottle of Cointreau over the lot. Wow!!! One of the guests spent half the afternoon gorging himself on them.

time to table - 1 hour
ingredients - to serve 6-8 people

2 punnets of fresh strawberries. English are the best, if not, use Welsh!
3 tablespoons of caster sugar
½ mug (100ml) Cointreau

1   Clean the strawberries and remove the stalks.
2   Cut into halves or quarters.
3   Place into a serving bowl and sprinkle with sugar.
4   Pour the Cointreau over the strawberries.
5   Cover and leave in the fridge for at least 1 hour so that the Cointreau and strawberry juices infuse into each other.

Serve the strawberries on their own with a small glass of Cointreau.

Photo: see page 132

tony's tip:

Absolutely no cream is needed with this dessert. Life will never be the same after this, believe me!!

tarte aux pommes

This tart is served the wrong way up. Or is it? In fact it looks spectacular when served, much more so than a British apple pie, where all you can see is the pastry. It can be stored frozen.

time to table - 1 hour
ingredients - to serve 6-8 people

For the sweet pastry:
2 mugs (400g, 12oz) plain flour
½ pack (125g) unsalted butter
4 tablespoons of granulated sugar
juice of 1 lemon
iced water
1 egg
For the apples:
3-4 large apples - Bramley or dessert
4-6 tablespoons of granulated sugar
juice of 1 lemon
1 jar of apricot jam

1   Sift the flour into a mixing bowl.
2   Add the butter in chunks and blend into the flour by hand until it forms a crumb-like mixture. Add the sugar and mix in with a fork.
3   Beat the egg, add the lemon juice and 2 tablespoons of iced water.
4   Add this to the flour gradually and mix in with a fork.
5   Then mould the pastry with your hands into a dough.
6   Leave in the fridge for 15-30 minutes to rest.
7   Put a little water with the lemon juice into a saucepan, and add the apricot jam.
8   Heat until the jam has melted and blended in with the lemon juice. Put aside to cool.
9   Meanwhile peel, quarter and core the apples, storing them in water with the rind of the lemon until needed.
10 Flour the work surface and roll out the pastry to fit a flat flan dish.
11 Roll it on to the rolling pin and carefully place it into a buttered flan dish.
12 Mould it into the dish, clean off the edges and fork the centre well.
13 The pastry can be cooked first 'blind' for 20 minutes in a mild oven at 160°C (320°F, gas mark 3) if you wish.
14 Drain the apple quarters and cut them into thin slices.
15 Arrange these clockwise on the pastry, ring by ring until you reach the centre.
16 Sprinkle the sugar over the apples - 6 tablespoons if using cooking apples, 4 tablespoons if using dessert apples.
17 Pour over the melted jam and lemon juice.
18 Bake in a medium oven at 160°C (320°F, gas mark 3) for 30 minutes until the apples are just beginning to brown. Put aside to rest.

Serve warm or cold with a small glass of Normandy Calvar.

I use a variety of sweet pastries for my desserts, but my favourite is pate sucré. The French often do things upside down. This is the classic upside down French apple tart, cooked with the pastry on top, and turned upside down to serve. It is perfectly moist on its own, and you can then really enjoy the flavour of the apples.

time to table - 1 hour
ingredients - to serve 6-8 people

For the pate sucré:
2/3 pack (150g) unsalted butter, clarified
4 tablespoons of caster sugar
2 medium sized eggs
2 mugs (400g, 12oz) plain flour
For the apples:
1/3 pack (100g) butter, clarified
6 dessert apples
4 tablespoons of sugar
1 teaspoon of grated nutmeg
juice of 1 lemon

1   Soften the butter in a microwave for a few seconds, and mix it in a mixing bowl with a fork until creamy.

2   Mix in the sugar and then the eggs.

3   Sift over the flour and blend it into the mix with a fork.

4   Finally mould it with your hands and put in the fridge to rest for 15-30 minutes.

5   Meanwhile peel, quarter and core the apples. Store in water with a piece of lemon to prevent browning.

6   Melt 100g butter in a round, 25cm wide baking dish.

7   Add the 4 tablespoons of sugar, and mix, allowing the sugar to caramelise slightly.

8   Place the apple quarters carefully around the dish.

9   Shake carefully as the sugar begins to caramelise.

10   Sprinkle the nutmeg over and then the lemon juice. Remove from the heat.

11   Flour a work surface and roll out the pate sucré.

12   Roll it onto a floured rolling pin. It will be a little sticky, but don't worry.

13   Roll it out over the apples, tucking in the excess around the sides. Prick well with a fork.

14   Bake in a medium to hot oven at 170°C (340°F, gas mark 3-4) for 30 minutes until the pastry is light brown.

15   Remove from the oven and allow it to cool for 5 minutes.

16   Carefully clear the sides using a knife around the edge.

17   Place a serving plate on top of the pastry.

18   Invert carefully and tap the bottom of the dish.

19   The tarte tartin should fall onto the plate, with the apples facing upwards, golden brown.

Serve hot or cold with a small glass of Normandy Calvar. Lovely.

some dinner party menus

Menu 1

Menu item
- Garlic mushrooms cooked in olive oil
- Faux coquilles St Jacques made with white wine and shallots, and coated with home made bread crumbs.
- Lemon sorbet
- Grilled fillet steak, with a pepper and red wine sauce, flambéed in brandy with jacket potatoes or Pommes de terre Lyonaisse
- Salad with French dressing, and French cheese if you dare!
- Fresh fruit salad or mousse au chocolate made with real dark chocolate and no cream
- Real black coffee or lemon tea, with chocolate truffles

Drink suggestion
- Sancerre
- Chardonnay

- Iced water
- Margaux or Chilean Merlot

- Côtes du Rhône
- Muscat or rum

- Rum

Menu 2

Menu item
- Chicken bites.
- Smoked salmon and shrimp parcels in horseradish sauce
- Lemon sorbet
- Pork tenderloin au Provence
- Cheese (just a tiny bit)
- Strawberries in Cointreau
- Black coffee or tea, with a slice of apple and almond tart

Drink suggestion
- Chilled Chablis
- Beaujolais
- Iced water
- Côtes du Rhône
- Côtes du Rhône
- Cointreau
- Cognac

Menu 3

Menu item
- Pepper and courgette soup
- Stuffed mushrooms
- Roast whole salmon

- Salad
- Cheese
- Tarte aux pommes
- Coffee or tea, with apple flapjack

Drink suggestion
- Muscadet
- Chardonnay
- Beaujolais or Côtes du Rhône

- Iced water
- Merlot or Côtes du Rhône
- Calvados
- Calvados

Here is a disaster menu for someone who is lactose intolerant.

Menu item
- Cream of mushroom soup
- Pork á la crème with cauliflower cheese and creamed mashed potatoes
- Salad dressed in mayonnaise made with cream
- Full cheese board
- Crème brûlée
- Cappuccino coffee with Belgian chocolates

❖   ❖   ❖

foods with and without lactose

Safe foods:
Coconut milk
Eggs
Fresh fish
Fresh fruit
Fresh meat, particularly organic (but beware ordinary chicken)
Fresh salad
Fresh seafood
Fresh vegetables
Freshly-squeezed fruit juice
Oat milk
Olive, groundnut and sunflower oils
Rice milk
Soya milk and associated products
Water (H$_2$O)

Foods to be wary of:
(Where milk products or lactose can be surprisingly found. Check the label very carefully. If in doubt, avoid.)
Bread
Breadcrumbs and batter, particularly when used to coat chicken and fish
Cakes, muffins, crumpets, doughnuts, pancakes, scones, biscuits and cookies
Cereal bars
Chocolate, both milk and plain
Cream, canned and packet soups
Custards
Drink powders
Flavoured crisps and some plain crisps
Instant hot drinks
Instant mashed potato
Low fat foods generally
Low fat mayonnaise
Margarine
Muesli
Paté
Pickles, sauces and relishes
Pie fillings
Pills (lactose is the 'filler' in many prescribed drugs and 10% of over-the-counter medicines)
Pizza
Powdered soups and sauces
Processed meats, including sausages, hot dogs, salamis and ham
Salad creams and dressings
Some breakfast cereals
Some lagers
Some chewy sweets
Stock cubes
Stout
Waffles

Think sugar

Lactose is the sugar in milk. It is made up of carbon, hydrogen and oxygen joined together to form a ring, with two sugars, galactose and glucose, stuck together (see **Figure 3**).

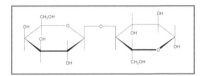

Figure 3. The chemical structure of lactose - ß galactose 1,4 glucose.

There is virtually no other sugar found in milk except lactose. Lactose arose in evolution some 200-300 million years ago, when dinosaurs still roamed the Earth. This was when the first mammals appeared. In fact lactose is only found in mammalian milk. Cow's milk contains nearly 50g per litre, equivalent to two large tablespoons. Human milk has even more, some 70g per litre. The word *lactose* originates from the Latin *Lac* = milk. It was discovered as long ago as 1666, though it took some 200 years before the exact chemical structure was known. People who are **intolerant** to lactose can't digest it properly. But people often tell us that they know someone who is **allergic** to milk. It is crucial to our story to understand the difference between these two medical conditions. In fact we regularly test our patients to check that they are not allergic to milk. But to understand an 'intolerance' we must first look at lactose itself, and why we scientists call it a sugar.

To most of us sugar is simply the crystalline substance that we have in a bowl on our breakfast table to sprinkle on our cornflakes, or to add to coffee and tea. This is true. But as you might expect it is not that simple. Science is very particular about how it names things. It is called the 'nomenclature'. International committees of scientists are set up regularly to discus the naming of molecules, and key numbers, such as the speed of light that is designated 'c', and so on. The sugar we keep in a bowl on our breakfast table is just one of hundreds of different substances that scientists call 'sugars'. We have taste buds on the back of our tongue that respond to these sugars. They taste sweet. At least some of them do. This sweet taste contrasts with our other four main tastes: bitter, sour, salt, and 'hot'. But in some cases a sugar may 'not be so sweet'. For example, paper is made from the sugar glucose. But if we chew on some paper it doesn't taste sweet at all, because the glucose is in the form of 'cellulose'. This molecule is the major constituent of the cell walls of plants, including trees. Cellulose is made of strings and strings of glucose molecules. Similarly, the starch we are familiar with as the white stuff in rice and potatoes is also made of strings and strings of glucose molecules. On its own, glucose tastes sweet. But when it is in a string, as it is in cellulose or starch, we can't taste anything obvious. It is not sweet. You can easily show this by an experiment you can have fun with in your own kitchen.

Imagine your favourite meal. Think very hard. Think sugar! You will begin to produce saliva as your mouth, and your digestive system, get ready to receive some delicious food. Now wash your mouth out with lukewarm water into a cup. Add some starch, which you can buy easily in the supermarket. Or you can try using a sliced potato with the white stuff, the starch, exposed. Touch a little of the cloudy liquid, or the surface of the potato, with your finger and taste. It will be virtually tasteless. Now leave the liquid or potato on the sideboard for about 15 minutes, and taste again. The cloudy liquid will have become clearer, and both the liquid and the surface of the potato should now taste a little sweet. Why? What has happened?

This simple biochemical experiment, in fact, holds the key to understanding lactose, and why so many people can't digest it properly. We can't directly absorb the starch we eat. But we can absorb glucose directly, in the gut. So the starch has to be split into its individual 'sugar' units - glucose, which we can then absorb. When you eat starch in rice or potatoes you release saliva. This contains an enzyme called amylase. This amylase breaks off the individual sugars units from the starch. Glucose tastes sweet, but the multi-glucose molecules of starch or cellulose in paper do not. We can't break down paper. But cows can. They use bacteria in their gut which have another enzyme, called cellulase. This breaks down the multi-sugar cellulose from the plant cell walls, and thus the cow can get energy from grass. Amazing isn't it? The link then with this story about starch and lactose is that in order to absorb lactose it too has to be broken into its individual sugars.

Sugars belong to a group of molecules called carbohydrates. These all contain three key atoms - carbon, hydrogen and oxygen. Some also contain nitrogen. All the atoms in a carbohydrate are linked together in a very special way. And it is all to do with the formula that we chemists use to write down their structures on paper. The formula is $C_xH_{2y}O_y$, where x and y are the number of carbon or oxygen atoms in the molecule. There are 2y hydrogens, *i.e.* twice as many as there are oxygens. As usual in science there are some exceptions to this rule, but essentially all the main carbohydrates that we eat have this general formula. In glucose, the main sugar in blood, x and y = 6, so its chemical formula is $C_6H_{12}O_6$. However in lactose x=12 and y=11, so its formula is $C_{12}H_{22}O_{11}$. Now perhaps we can begin to see why they are called carbohydrates. Many of us will be familiar with the term 'carbohydrate', and especially those on dietary regimes such as the Atkins diet. It is used generically to include all sugar type substances; e.g. glucose, sucrose, starch . . . and lactose. The key to the chemical structure of a 'carbohydrate' is water.

It was the research studies of a famous physicist in the eighteenth century called Henry Cavendish (1731-1810) that lead to the discovery of the structure of water. Cavendish found that water contained only hydrogen and oxygen, and by measuring very carefully how much hydrogen and oxygen it took to make a certain weight of water, it was found that every water molecule in the Universe has 2 hydrogens stuck on to one oxygen. The formula is H_2O. Now, if we look at the formula for glucose, *i.e.* $C_6H_{12}O_6$, it is simply $C_6(H_2O)_6$. We see that is has 6 carbon atoms and 6 water molecules. So it was logical to call it carbon-water, or carbo-hydrate, from *hudor* the Greek for water. In lactose the formula $C_{12}H_{22}O_{11}$ becomes $C_{12}(H_2O)_{11}$.

So how does this help us understand why lactose is a sugar, and why it is different from the sugar we add to our cornflakes? The key is how the carbon, hydrogen and oxygen atoms are arranged.

As we have already seen, lactose is galactose-glucose and has the formula $C_{12}H_{22}O_{11}$. But both glucose, and a number of other individual sugars such as galactose, have the same formula - $C_6H_{12}O_6$. The reason is that in each particular sugar the carbons, hydrogens and oxygens are arranged together in a different order (see **Figure 4** where each line represents a link between two atoms). When you link two sugars, such as galactose and glucose, together, one water H_2O is lost. To split them again water is added back. As a result, each sugar has slightly different properties in our bodies. So the proper scientific names of all sugars have the three letters **-ose** at the end; glucose, sucrose, fructose, lactose, cellulose and so on. Those that are single molecules, like glucose and fructose, we call these mono-saccharides, from the Greek *sakkaon* and the Latin *saccharum*, both meaning sugar. Those that have two sugars linked together are di-saccharides. Two glucoses make maltose, but glucose with fructose make sucrose. And galactose with glucose makes **lactose**. But this is not the end of it. You can find in nature molecules where three, four, even hundreds of sugars are all linked together to form what we call tri-, tetra- and poly-saccharides (see **Table 8**).

Table 8. Major sugars in our diet.

Sugar type	Specific sugar	Chemical formula	Structure	Example of food source
Mono-saccharide	Glucose	$C_6H_{12}O_6$	Single sugar	Some fresh fruits
	Galactose	$C_6H_{12}O_6$	Single sugar	Some fresh fruits
	Fructose	$C_6H_{12}O_6$	Single sugar	Some fresh fruits
Di-saccharide	Sucrose	$C_{12}H_{22}O_{11}$	Glucose-fructose	Sugar cane and all plants. Normal table sugar
	Lactose	$C_{12}H_{22}O_{11}$	Galactose-glucose	Only mammalian milk
	Maltose	$C_{12}H_{22}O_{11}$	Glucose-glucose	Malt-sugar, formed by the action of the enzyme diastase on starch
Tri-saccharide	Raffinose	$C_{18}H_{32}O_{16}$	Galactose-glucose-fructose	Beans, root vegetables
Tetra-saccharide	Stachyose	$C_{24}H_{42}O_{21}$	Galactose-galactose-glucose-fructose	Beans, root vegetables
Poly-saccharide	Starch	$(C_6H_{10}O_5)_n$	Hundreds of glucoses	Plants
	Cellulose	$(C_6H_{10}O_5)_n$	Hundreds of glucoses	Plants
	Glycogen	$(C_6H_{10}O_5)_n$	Hundreds of glucoses	Animal tissues

Raffinose and stachyose, the 'double whammy' sugars I discussed in the first section of this book are made up of three and four sugars respectively. Raffinose is galactose-glucose-fructose, and stachyose is galactose-galactose-glucose-fructose. These cannot be broken down in the small intestine, and they block the uptake of glucose into the blood. The result is a feast for the bacteria in the large intestine.

Lactase

As I discussed at the beginning of the book, lactase is the enzyme in the small intestine that breaks lactose into its two sugars, galactose and glucose, so that these can then be absorbed into the blood stream. Lactase is a protein, and because it catalyses a chemical reaction it is an enzyme. It is unique in its formation, location and catalytic activity. It is first formed inside the cells that line the small intestine as a protein chain of 1,927 amino acids. Then it has to be processed by the cell. Several sugar molecules are attached to the protein, and it is chopped approximately in two, one half being discarded. The remainder is taken to the outer membrane of the cell, where a further few amino acids are cropped off, leaving a final protein of 1,059 amino acids. The final enzyme consists of two of these tightly stuck together. Lactase is highly unusual as an enzyme since it has two distinct active sites within one protein molecule. Only one of these sites breaks lactose in two. Monkeys don't keep cattle, so we could safely lose this on weaning during evolution since, without a dairy herd, there would be no source of lactose other than the mother's breast.

So why don't we get rid of all of our lactase after weaning?

The reason is that, interestingly, we need the 'other site', the one that does not break down lactose. This is why no one loses all of their lactase. This 'other site' breaks down fats called cerebrosides, giving us an important source of a substance called sphingosine, vital in the brain. It also gives us an important source of vitamin B6. This 'other site' was first discovered by biochemists who were studying a remarkable substance called phlorizin, that had been found in apple tree bark. Many of our current day pharmaceuticals originated as toxins in plants. Phlorizin was being studied because it can cause diabetes. The 'other site' in lactase cleaves phlorizin in two. Thus the correct scientific name for lactase is lactase phlorizin-hydrolase - LPH for short. Scientists give it an EC number, EC standing for Enzyme Commission. Because lactase has two active sites it has two numbers - EC 3.2.1.62 and 3.2.1.108. The number EC 3.2.1.23 has been mistakenly used for lactase in some publications. This is the EC number for a bacterial enzyme called ß-galactosidase. It is the enzyme in bacteria that digests lactose, but is a completely different protein from lactase. Lactase is only found in the small intestine of mammals. It starts to rise in the duodenum, peaks in the jejunum and falls off gradually down the ileum. The small intestine (**Figure 5**) is an incredible organ, responsible for digesting and then absorbing all our food. It is folded, folded and folded again. It has a surface area half the size of a football pitch. Incredible!

All animals, except white Northern Europeans and a few tribes in Africa and Asia, lose 75-90% of the enzyme lactase within a few years of weaning. The final level and time course of this loss vary considerably with each ethnic group. Chinese and Japanese lose 80-90% within 3-4 years of weaning, whereas Asians and Jews can retain some 20-30% as adults, taking several years to reach this level.

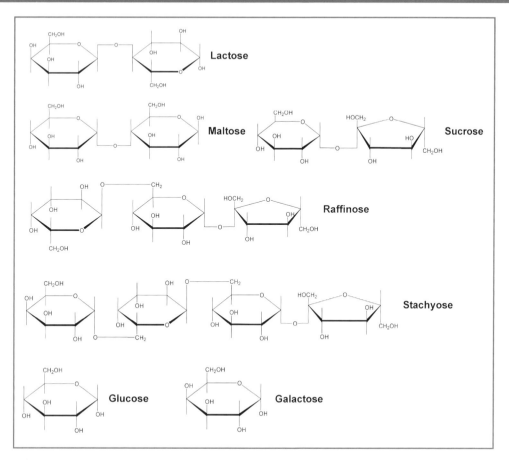

Figure 4. Common sugars shown with the atoms arranged in space.

The 10% or so of white Northern Europeans who lose lactase after weaning can take 18-20 years to reach their nadir. Thus most Chinese, Japanese, Asians, black Africans, Red Indians, and Jews are hypolactasic (see **Table 1**). They are the norm as far as lactase is concerned. In fact, it has been estimated that over 30% of the adult population in the USA also have a low lactase, and that as many as two-thirds of the world's adult population, *i.e.* some **4,000** million people, are the same. All of these people are thus potentially lactose intolerant. Though most can still take some milk with no ill-effects.

The mechanism causing the loss of lactase on weaning is still unknown. Many studies have looked at the DNA in the lactase gene itself, and the DNA next to it that controls whether it is switched on. But no consistent differences have been found between people who retain their lactase into adulthood and those who lose it after weaning. DNA is of course a long string of four bases, A, T, G and C, forming the computer programme that codes for proteins. The lactase gene is found on chromosome 2 and is quite big, being over 50,000 bases long. In 2002, a Finnish group had a break-though. By careful genetic analysis and sequencing of the DNA upstream from the lactase gene they found two mutations that correlated perfectly with hypolactasia - low lactase. One was a change from a T to C, 13,910 bases up from the start of lactase, and the other a change from A to

G, a little further away, 22,018 bases upstream from lactase itself. We all have two pairs of chromosomes, one set from our mother the other from our father. There were thus six genetic types - CC/GG, CT/GG, CC/GA, TC/GG, TT/GC and TT/AA. The Finnish group found that CC/GG was always associated with low lactase and thus lactose intolerance. We have carried out a major clinical study correlating these DNA types with lactose intolerance. We have shown that they provide an important aid to the diagnosis and the management of lactose intolerance. But these DNA differences still don't explain the loss of lactase on weaning, because we have found several families now with both the T and A who are also lactose intolerant.

Based on the genetic predisposition, homozygous CC/GG have low lactase, those who are homozygous TT/AA are lactase persistent, and those who are heterozygous CT/GA are intermediate. But our analysis of these two polymorphisms suggests that heterozygotes can still have severe lactose intolerance. And we have found several TT/AA families with lactose intolerance. Therefore, this polymorphism cannot explain completely hypolactasia, and thus lactose intolerance.

Dairying is less than 8,000 years old, though there is evidence that cheese-making may go back earlier than this. So the ability to digest lactose fully in adulthood must have played a major part in the white population moving up into the plains of Europe that began some 10,000 years ago, after the last ice age had finished.

How lactose intolerance causes symptoms - The bacterial toxin hypothesis

Any food not digested and absorbed in the small intestine naturally ends up in the next compartment of the gut - the large intestine. This is a huge culture of bacteria. Over 50% of faeces are made from their remains. It has been estimated that there may be as many as 100 times as many bacterial cells here as there are our own cells in the rest of the body, and over 400 bacterial species, many of which have still to be properly identified. There is not much oxygen here. As a result, many of the bacteria found in the large intestine can't survive in oxygen at all. This is why it has been difficult to identify them using normal culture techniques. There are two main types of bacteria in the gut: the eubacteria and the archaebacteria. The latter aren't really bacteria at all. Yes they are single celled, but they belong to a completely different group of micro-organisms from the bacteria with which we are most familiar. They are evolutionary-wise very ancient and called the Archae. They often live in very hostile environments, such as hot springs, acid and alkaline lakes, and high salt ponds. And they can produce methane gas, while the eubacteria can make hydrogen. Quite an explosive mix!

Bacteria can release an extraordinary number of different types of molecules (**Table 9**). The crucial ones in lactose intolerance are the gases and metabolites, though the others now need full investigation. Most of the cells in our body need oxygen. They 'burn' without making fire. The hydrogen trapped in substances we eat, such as sugars and fats, is 'burnt' giving us the energy we need to survive and do things. Water is the product. But down in the low oxygen environment of the large intestine, cells cannot make use of the energy trapped in the hydrogen of sugars by 'burning' it. There is not enough oxygen. Therefore, they have to get rid of the hydrogen another way. They do this either by making hydrogen gas itself, the main gas of flatus, or by producing alcohols, aldehydes and acids. The hydrogen gas acts as a substrate for the archaebacteria to make methane. We have now shown that measuring hydrogen and methane in the breath, coupled with detection of the genetics, improves diagnosis of lactose intolerance from less than 50%, with old style approach, to greater than 75% using our method. But it is the metabolites we propose are the main culprits in causing the symptoms after eating lactose.

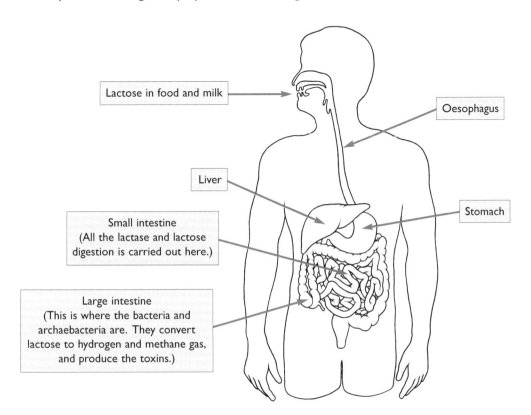

183

Figure 5. The human alimentary tract where we digest and then absorb our food.
The small intestine is some 6-7 metres long, and consists of three parts: the duodenum (5-6cm), which leads to the jejunum (2.5m), which leads to the ileum (4m). This then connects with the large intestine. The enzyme lactase, which cleaves lactose into the sugars galactose and glucose, is highest in the jejunum, tailing off through the ileum, with just a little in the duodenum.

The gases cause the gut to distend, and are the cause of gut pain. But it is the metabolites that are absorbed to 'hit' the tissues around the body, such as the brain, heart, muscle, joints, and immune system. We propose these toxic metabolites (**Figure 6**) include - acetaldehyde, acetoin, butan 2,3 diol, dimethyl glyoxal, diacetyl, ethanol, formate, methane, propan 1,3 diol, indoles, skatoles, spermine and short chain fatty acids, as well as peptide and protein toxins. Lactose itself, and galactose, could also be toxic if absorbed into the blood stream. The bacterial toxins are primitive signalling molecules. They act on pathways that switch cells on or off in the nervous system, heart and muscles, and the immune system. Conventionally, lactose intolerance causes diarrhoea *via* an osmotic mechanism, *i.e.* by pulling water out of the body. But we found in many patients diarrhoea did not start until 24 hours after the lactose load, and could persist for days, long after the lactose had gone. Therefore, it is likely that lactose-induced diarrhoea is really caused by a signalling mechanism analogous to cholera- or entero-toxin.

Table 9. Substances that can be released by different bacteria and archaebacteria.

Product released	Example
Gases	Carbon dioxide, hydrogen, methane, hydrogen sulphide, oxygen, nitrogen, ammonia
Ions	Calcium, sodium, potassium, magnesium, manganese, iron
Metabolites	Alcohols, diols, aldehydes, short chain fatty acids, dimethyl hydrazine, amino acid degradation products, cyclic AMP
Vitamins	K, B12, thiamine, riboflavin
Pheremones	Lactones, cytokines
Small molecule toxins	Antibiotics, tetrodotoxin
Drugs	Many
Peptides	Toxins, enzymes
Nucleic acids	Competence factors, plasmids, bacteriophages (= viruses)
Polymers	Poly hydroxybutyrate

Note: Any particular bacterium can only release some of these.

Bacterial putrefaction in the colon as a pathogen was first proposed over 100 years ago by a protégé of Louis Pasteur in Paris, the Russian scientist Elie Metchnikoff (1845-1916). Metchnikoff won the Nobel Prize for Physiology or Medicine with Paul Ehrlich in 1908 for discovering the 'waste disposal' system in our body, called phagocytes. These are crucial when we have to combat an infection. But Metchnikoff's real intellectual 'baby' was his bacterial hypothesis. **Sym**biosis means organisms living with each other, usually in harmony. But Metchnikoff believed in **dys**biosis, meaning not in harmony. He argued that bacterial putrefaction in the gut was the cause of all disease. Quite a claim! But we believe he was on the right track. This work has been forgotten.

The problem was that there was no mechanism to explain how the putative toxins, he suggested were released by gut bacteria, could cause damage to cells and tissues in the rest of the body. We now have a mechanism. We have established an invertebrate model system, the water flea *Daphnia pulex*, to investigate this hypothesis. And being even bolder, we hope that this hypothesis will lead to a new path to the real cause of rheumatoid arthritis, diabetes, multiple sclerosis, and some cancers. We believe it is going to revolutionise our approach to discovering the cause of these diseases where research into the real cause is floundering, and where there is some published evidence for a link between the occurrence of the disease and milk consumption (see

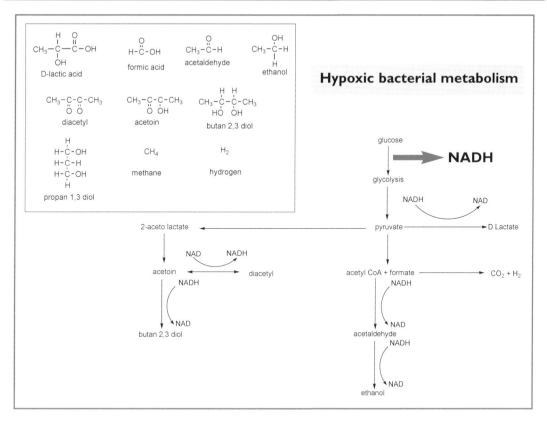

Figure 6. How bacteria can produce the toxins.
The toxins are listed in the top left box. Hypoxic = low oxygen. NADH = the substance that normally 'burns' the hydrogen initially trapped in the sugar molecules.

'Further Reading'). Why is there an epidemic in type 2 diabetes in the Asian population? Could it be that this ethnic group has westernised its diet. Many Indian restaurants now use milk and cream, full of lactose, instead of the correct ingredient, coconut milk, that has no lactose.

Leaky Gut Syndrome
The term 'leaky gut syndrome' is used to describe symptoms caused by a 'leaky' gut. The idea is that spaces develop in the gut wall allowing toxins, food and even bacteria to 'leak' into the blood. There have been several books written about this (see **'Further Reading'**), and details can be found on several web sites. Many of the symptoms listed as 'leaky gut' are identical to the ones I described for systemic lactose intolerance. But the concept of 'leaky gut syndrome' is not accepted medically. Nor is there any convincing evidence that there is a mechanism to explain it. As we show here, the symptoms allocated to a 'leaky gut' are better explained by our bacterial toxin hypothesis.

The new clinical test for lactose intolerance
When a patient presents with unexplained irritable bowel (IBS), it is essential first to carry out a genetic analysis. Then, if necessary, a test for both breath hydrogen and methane for up to 6 hours,

recording the severity of any symptoms, after taking 50g lactose (1g/kg if you weigh less than 50kg), should be undertaken. The current test for lactose intolerance, involving measurement of breath hydrogen following oral ingestion of lactose, fails to detect less than 50% of cases because the test lacks specificity and sensitivity, and does not require a record of both gut and symptoms around the body (systemic). Also, until now, there has been no established genetic test for lactose intolerance. We have shown that the two polymorphisms C/T_{13910} and G/A_{22018} on chromosome 2, closely linked to hypolactasia, correlate with breath hydrogen and methane and both gut and systemic symptoms caused by lactose. The genetic test, coupled with a detailed record of gut and systemic symptoms for 48 hours after lactose and an extension of the breath hydrogen and methane test to 6 hours, provide a new approach to the clinical management of lactose intolerance and irritable bowel syndrome (see **Table 10**). Patients diagnosed as lactose intolerant must be advised how to come off lactose completely, and be warned of 'risk' foods inadequately labelled, some including processed meats, bread, cake mixes, some soft drinks and some lagers.

All our CC_{13910}/GG_{22018} patients were severely lactose intolerant. Detection of this genotype avoids severe symptoms induced by the lactose challenge. Analysis of C/T_{13910} only is required since G/A_{22018} had identical correlations. The CC patients complained mainly of gut-related symptoms after lactose, consistent with 100% having high breath hydrogen. The CT/GA and TT/AA patients also suffered gut symptoms during the lactose test, but complained particularly of systemic symptoms, such as severe headache, fatigue and palpitations. This explains the confusion in diagnosis. Our data refute the claim that the breath hydrogen test alone should be the 'gold standard' test for lactose intolerance. Prolonging the analysis to 6 hours improved detection of lactose intolerance, but still more than 40% were missed. Elevated breath methane improved the sensitivity of detecting lactose intolerance, and a third of patients with lactose intolerance could have raised breath methane without raised breath hydrogen. This was consistent with hydrogen being the substrate for methane production.

Thus, a patient presenting with unexplained gut and/or systemic symptoms (IBS) should first be tested for the polymorphism C/T_{13910}. This is done analysing the DNA from a small blood sample, or by scraping a few cells from inside the cheek using a tiny brush. All CC should change to a lactose free diet. CT or TT patients should undergo a 6 hour hydrogen and methane breath test, recording symptom severity for 48 hours. Gut infections, such as *Giardia* or rotavirus, or hormonal imbalance, should be investigated if there is no evidence of family history. If the breath hydrogen or methane is positive, *i.e.* greater than 20 parts per million (ppm) or greater than 5ppm over the nadir respectively, advice on how to change to a lactose free diet should be given. Patients with a negative breath test and a significant increase in symptoms after the lactose load should undergo a supervised trial to determine their lactose threshold. Every patient should be followed-up in 12 weeks for a definitive diagnosis. It is vital to advise on calcium and vitamin D status, and the use of probiotics that we are often asked about by our patients. Probiotics are live bacteria that you can eat, and will metabolise lactose to lactic acid. This diverts the lactose away from the toxin pathways in the colonic bacteria. *Lactobacillus* and other probiotics are available in many health food shops. Try them. We find they often improve gut movement and make you feel better if you have any form of food intolerance. However, it is not clear whether probiotics allow someone who is lactose intolerant to take more lactose than they can normally cope with. Such dietary

Table 10. Our recommended clinical management to investigate patients for lactose intolerance.

1 Patient referred for lactose tolerance test.
2 Buccal (swab inside the mouth) sample for genetic analysis. A patient presenting with unexplained gut and/or systemic symptoms should first be tested for the polymorphism C/T_{13910}:
   a. If CC immediate removal of all lactose from diet. If symptoms improve after one month diagnosis of lactose intolerance confirmed.
   b. If CT or TT carry out lactose tolerance test.
3 New recommended lactose tolerance test:
   a. 50g (1g/kg for children) lactose, taken dissolved in a mug of water (200ml).
   b. Record breath hydrogen and methane every 30 minutes for 3 hours, then hourly up to 6 hours.
   c. Record all symptoms for 48 hours.
   d. If the breath test is positive, advice to change to a lactose free diet is given.
   e. Every patient should be followed-up in 12 weeks for a definitive diagnosis. If the symptoms present on referral have significantly improved then the diagnosis of lactose intolerance is made.
   f. If the breath test is negative, but there is a significant increase in symptoms after the lactose load, the patient should undergo a supervised trial to determine their lactose threshold.
   g. Family studies should be carried out to determine other affected individuals.
   h. Hypolactasia caused by infections, such as *Giardia* or rotavirus, should be investigated if there is no evidence of family history.
4 Give advice on lactose free meals, and the danger of 'hidden' lactose.
5 Follow-up in 1 year.
6 Calcium and vitamin D status should be monitored, and patient advised on the use of probiotics.
7 Advise patient to keep a food diary, so that they can find the culprit if they get caught out.

Note: If you want to be tested for lactose intolerance ask your GP. If your GP is not sure what to do, see our web site or get the GP to contact us.

'lactase' with lactose can reduce breath hydrogen and gut symptoms, but the long-term benefits are unclear. You can also buy 'lactase' tablets to add yourself to milk to reduce the lactose content.

Who should you believe?

We live in an era where most active people have financial and other interests in some commercial organisation or other. This is just as true for scientists and doctors, particularly in research, where funding is difficult to find. The Press are quick to find whether experts presenting evidence through the media have conflicts of interest, and if they are involved with, or have funding from, for example

187

the pharmaceutical or drinks industries, or have shares in a Company producing GM food. Likewise the Dairy Industry has a powerful lobby. It funds many scientific studies world-wide, and photos of medical scientists can be found on web sites. There are many papers in the scientific literature dealing with milk and lactose, where some of the funding for these studies has come either directly or indirectly from the dairy industry, or from an organisation promoting milk and dairy products. Of course, there is nothing wrong in this.

However, in our open modern age it is important that all scientific papers and peer reviewers declare whether they have any links that might be perceived as a conflict of interest, just as MPs do when they declare all financial interests at the House of Commons. Then anyone can assess whether there was any bias in the way the authors have acted or presented their views. Many top scientific and medical journals now insist that authors declare whether they have any financial or other interests that might be seen to affect the objectivity of their work. But this was not always the case. So, when you are reading a scientific paper, or an article about milk, dairy products, lactose or related foods, be aware of this, and check that the authors have no potential conflicts. Most scientists value their integrity above all, as I do. Very, very few are ever deliberately dishonest. But we all have human frailty. When we have an interest in something we must declare it. Stephanie and I believe we have no conflicts.

So how do we know we are right?

All the evidence Stephanie and I have accumulated over the past six years shows that large numbers of patients have IBS because they are lactose intolerant. Their symptoms had a genuine organic cause and were not psychosomatic, as has often been claimed. Furthermore, their dramatic improvement cannot be explained by the so-called 'placebo' effect. There has been much written about the 'placebo' effect of drugs and other medical remedies. This is the psychological effect of a medical therapy.

The dramatic, sustained symptom reduction in our patients on a true lactose free diet cannot be explained by such a 'placebo' effect. Many studies assessing the validity of a clinical intervention use a double blind, randomised, placebo-controlled trial to remove bias. Everyone in the study takes both the drug and a placebo in random order, and the scientists don't know in which order they have been taken until all the data have been analysed. But the efficacy of this has been questioned. Many of our patients suffer severe symptoms after the lactose intolerance test. We believe it is unethical to put them through unnecessary suffering. It is impossible to find a substitute to lactose that prevents many subjects guessing whether they are taking lactose or not. A substance called aspartame has been used as an alternative sweetener in some studies. But aspartame can cause a range of allergic, cardiovascular, endocrine and neurological symptoms.

Our studies have been based on rigorous clinical criteria. DNA analysis was undertaken blind, and precautions were taken to minimize bias in the data analysis. Crucially it is impossible to 'blind' dietary **removal**. We now have over 500 patients with dramatic improvement in both gut and systemic symptoms, sustained over more than one year, following complete dietary removal of lactose. In patients diagnosed with lactose intolerance the average number of symptoms dropped from 9 to 1 when they excluded lactose from their diet. This cannot be explained by a placebo effect. Symptoms only returned when the patient unknowingly ingested food containing 'hidden' lactose (see **Figure 7**). Crucially, we have measured 'hidden' lactose.

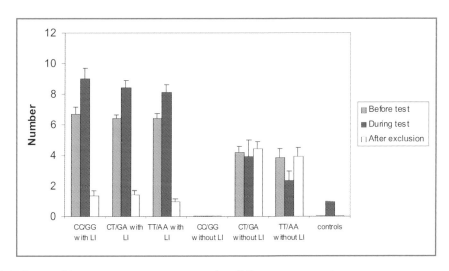

Figure 7. Effect of lactose on symptoms in different genetic groups.
Number of symptoms reported before and after 50g of lactose. LI = lactose intolerance.

On to the future

I hope this trip into the wonders of science has helped you to understand the complexities of lactose intolerance. Science has been my life for over 50 years. I still get a thrill every time I set up a new experiment, and I always await the results in anticipation. There is still much to learn about lactose and lactose intolerance. One thing puzzled me early on in my quest to unravel the mysterious symptoms caused by lactose. The question that struck me was: why would anyone want to add lactose to foods and drinks? Why not use sucrose? It suddenly struck me that perhaps yeast can't metabolise lactose. So, I set up an experiment with some brewer's yeast. I made up a slurry of the yeast in some water, with a little added salts, and then added various sugars to see what happened. If the yeast was able to eat up the particular sugar then carbon dioxide would be released. I set up a little bubble counter on top of the bottle containing the yeast and the sugar. The results are shown in **Figure 8**, and are quite dramatic. Yeast metabolises sucrose and glucose quite happily. But there was virtually no carbon dioxide produced when I added lactose to the yeast. Q.E.D.

Scientists don't have a great reputation for being entrepreneurs. Maybe we don't like taking risks with money. But we take risks every day when we do an experiment. It might not work! Six years ago I took a huge professional risk when I decided to focus my entire research effort on lactose intolerance. It was the right decision, as it has now brought together all my research interests and technologies - cell signalling, Darwin, and bioluminescence - into one problem. Here are the three key questions that I am trying to answer:
1. What are the toxins released by gut bacteria and how do they work?
2. What is the mechanism of losing lactase after weaning?
3. How did lactose evolve?

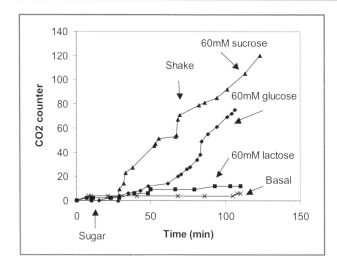

Figure 8. Metabolism of sugars by yeast.
5g of dried bakers yeast was made as a 10ml slurry in a simple salt medium (50mM MOPS, 25mM NaCl, 2mM KCl, 2mM CaCl₂, 1mM MgCl₂, 1mM NaHCO₃, pH 7.0) containing no added nutrients. 2ml of this slurry was then added to 50mM of the salt medium and 60mM of sugar added (◆) = glucose; (▲) = sucrose; (■) = lactose; (X) = control (basal) with nothing added. The metabolism was monitored by CO_2 production measured using a 'U' tube filled with water and a bubble counter (NCBE, Reading). Results were plotted as the number of bubbles against time.

I have set up a major project to look for the putative toxins in samples taken before and after the lactose tolerance test. Over the past twenty years I have established a way of using the DNA from glow-worms and other amazing creatures that emit their own light to light up chemical processes in live cells. Using genetic engineering in the test tube, the glow-worm DNA can be incorporated into a human cell. This cell will then glow in the dark. When a particular chemical reaction occurs in the cell, the light emitted goes up or down, and can change colour, a process I call the 'Rainbow effect'. Finding out how nature has given us a complete rainbow of colours in bioluminescence lead me to invent 'Rainbow proteins' that change colour when they react with a substance I wanted to measure. The result is that one can now watch tiny puffs of calcium and other chemicals going in and out of cells, when the cells are attacked by the bacterial toxins produced during lactose intolerance.

The key to any advance in medicine is 'mechanism', what causes particular symptoms and other aspects of an illness to occur? Such medical advances over the past two centuries have relied heavily on 'model' systems. These enable scientists to discover mechanisms using experiments that could not be carried out in human beings. Hence the plethora of Nobel Prizes using such model systems to understand such diverse processes such as the brain, genetics and cancer. Model organisms include a squid, the fruit fly and a tiny worm, and even yeast.

So, I have developed an extraordinary model to look for the toxins that cause heart palpitations in about a quarter of our patients. My model is a water flea called *Daphnia* (**Figure 9**). It has a heart just 0.1 millimetre long and responds to substances that affect the human heart simply by adding them to the water in which they are swimming. I was very excited when I discovered that adding lactose in this way caused the heart of *Daphnia* to become arrhythmic.

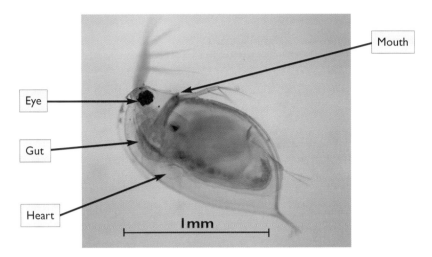

Figure 9. The water flea *Daphnia pulex*.

What Darwin missed

Life began on this planet about 3,600 million years ago. The first living things were single celled. These eventually evolved into the millions of species of multi-celled animals and plants, as well as tens of thousands of different microbes. This is the process of evolution, and was first written down in scientific language by Erasmus Darwin (1731-1802), the grandfather of Charles. Erasmus was one of the great polymaths of the eighteenth century. He was probably the best doctor in England, a scientist, an inventor, and a poet. He was also a founder of a group called the Lunar Society that set up the industrial revolution. Erasmus was a genius. Although he did not use the word evolution, he explained how single cells developed over a long period of the Earth's history into the multi-celled organisms we see today. He did this in a medical book he called 'Zoonomia', and an incredible poem called the 'Temple of Nature'. Since his time there has been a terrible amount of confusion about what we now call the process of evolution. Some 60 years after Erasmus had explained this process, his now more famous grandson Charles Darwin (1809-1882) and the naturalist Alfred Russel Wallace (1823-1913) brilliantly revealed the force that drove it - natural selection.

This is not a theory, as is often mistakenly described. Rather, natural selection is a **principle** that we apply to the **process** of evolution. It is a universal scientific truth. It works. My research group use it every day when carrying out genetic engineering experiments. But the question is: does natural selection explain everything about evolution? I think not, nor did Darwin himself. He wrote about his doubts in Chapter IV of 'The Origin of Species' - Difficulties on Theory. Surprisingly, Darwin missed a key aspect of our own evolution. In neither 'The Origin' nor 'The Descent of Man' is there mention of the crucial Rubicon that was crossed in our own evolution - the production of milk.

Natura non facit saltum - Nature takes no leaps, Darwin wrote in 'The Origin of Species'. But was he right? Which came first, the sugar lactose or lactase - the enzyme we have to have if we are to digest lactose? This is an example that I believe is the key question facing biology today. Using the analogy of computer language, when is a process digital and when is it analogue? When Darwin returned from his Beagle voyage, he realised the importance of the finches he had observed on the Galapagos islands. Separated geographical on different islands, they had evolved to have different beaks. That's fine if a species is separated for long enough. But the problem he didn't solve was, how do you get two finches from one, when all the individuals are living on the same island in the same environment? Biochemistry can now answer this fundamental problem in understanding evolution. The answer lies in biodiversity.

Conventionally there are three types of biodiversity, essential for the survival of an ecosystem:

- Diversity of species
- Diversity of genetics
- Diversity of habitats

But there is a fourth, and the one that is the key to evolution and how it can lead to two separate species from one. I call it molecular biodiversity. I have written about this in more depth in my book 'Rubicon', and in an article I wrote after a lecture I gave to the British Ecological Society - 'Save those Molecules' (see **'Further Reading'**). The diversity of the amount of lactase that is found within the human population is just one example of such molecular biodiversity. Bioluminescence - natural light emission from animals and microbes - is another.

So, there are two key questions relating to genome projects we now have to ask:
- How does a new protein, such as lactase, or a process such as lactose production, originate and develop **before** it can respond to the force of natural selection?
- Why are there so many 'bad' genes in the population? The principle revealed by Darwin and Wallace tells us that each must have a selective advantage, otherwise natural selection would have removed them.

What started for me as a personal quest to solve an illness that was devastating my family, so that we could have our lives back, has lead me to the greatest controversy in biology. This was why I decided to switch my entire research effort to it. Darwin missed his own lactose intolerance. Hardly surprising, since this condition wasn't known medically in the nineteenth century. But Darwin missed something else, even closer to his 'heart'. The science of lactose intolerance can reveal the answer to the question Darwin never really addressed, *i.e.* the true 'origin' rather than the 'development' of the human species.

Information about the Dairy Industry, Lactose and Lactose Intolerance

www.welstonpress.com
Our web site. The only one at present that deals with systemic symptoms caused by lactose.

www.lactose.co.uk
Conventional information about lactose intolerance and selling products.

www.lactoseintolerance.co.uk
Conventional information about lactose intolerance and milk allergies, with symptoms, treatments, and 'hidden' milk products.

www.lactoseintolerant.org
Conventional information only about lactose intolerance and milk allergies.

www.milksucks.com
Arguments against taking milk and dairy products, including ethical treatment of animals.

www.lactaid.com
Product for alleviating lactose intolerance.

www.NOTMILK.com
Web site for Milk: the deadly poison.

www.windsorbookshop.co.uk
Our local bookshop, Windsor Bookshop, and distributor for Welston Press.

www.amazon.com
Excellent general book site.

www.nationaldairycouncil.org
US Dairy Council site.

Information about Lactolite - a product with reduced lactose, made from milk.
www.arlafoods.co.uk

Soya and Oat Milk Sites
www.soyafoods.com
Major distributor of soya milk products.

www.oatly.com
Manufacturer of oat milk. A site with cooking ideas.

www.alprosoya.co.uk
Soya and dairy free products.

GM Food Testing Sites

www.debatabase.org
General information about GM foods and testing.

www.tepnel.com
Tepnel Biosystems who offer tests for GM in food to ensure compliance with European Regulations on the labelling of Genetically Modified (GM) foods and helps manufacturers avoid contamination by GM ingredients that are not approved.

Lactose Suppliers Sites

These make interesting reading. It is worth looking at these sites, to see where they say the lactose is used.
www.lactose.co.nz

www.lactose.co.uk

www.parktonks.co.uk

www.wheysystems.com/prod.htm

❖   ❖   ❖

Books

1   Aurrichio S, Semnza G, Editors (1993). Common food intolerances 2: Milk in human nutrition and adult-type hypolactasia. Dyn Nutr Res. Karger, Basel.

2   Brostoff, J and Challacombe, SJ (2002) Editors. Food allergy and intolerance. Saunders, London, 2nd edition. ISBN 0702020389.

3   Brostoff, J and Gamlin, L (1989). The complete guide to food allergy and intolerance. Bloomsbury, London. ISBN 0-7475-0242-0.

4   Burlant, A (1996). Secrets of lactose-free cooking. Avery Publishing Group, New York. ISBN 0-89529-724-8. [Over 150 recipes of dairy-free and lactose-reduced meals from breakfast to dinner.]

5   Campbell, AK (1994). Rubicon: the fifth dimension of biology. Duckworth, London. Now available from Welston Press on CD-ROM. ISBN 0-7156-2499-7.

6   Campbell, AK and Matthews, SB (2001). Lactose intolerance and the MATHS syndrome: what are they and how can I cope? Welston Press, Pembrokeshire. ISBN 0-9540866-0-0.

7   Carper, S. (1995). Milk is not for everybody. Living with lactose intolerance. Facts On File, New York. ISBN 0-8160-3127-4.

8   Cohen R (1997). Milk: the deadly poison. Argus Publishing, New Jersey, USA. ISBN 0-9659196-0-9.

9   Colp, R (1977). To be an invalid: the illness of Charles Darwin. University of Chicago, Chicago and London.

10   Hall, PA (1998). 101 Fabulous dairy free desserts everyone will love. For the lactose intolerant, the dairy allergic and their friends and families. Station Hill Openings, Barrytown, USA. ISBN 1-58177-018-9.

11   Jelliffe, DN and Jelluffe, EFP (1978). Human milk in the modern world. Oxford University Press, Oxford. ISBN 0-19-264919-1.

12   Le Fanu, J (1999). The rise and fall of modern medicine. Little, Brown and Co, and Abacus, London. ISBN 0-349-11280-0.

13   Knox, L and Lowman, S (2000). Great healthy food lactose-free. Carrol and Brown, London. ISBN 1-903258-07-3.

14   Metchnikoff, E (1908). The nature of man. Studies in optimistic philosophy. English translation edited by P Charles Mitchell. GP Putnam's Sons, New York and London. [See p73 for his bacterial putrefaction hypothesis.]

15   Miller, GD, Jarvis, JK and McBean, LD (2000). Handbook of dairy foods and nutrition. 2nd edition. National Dairy Council, Washington. ISBN 0-8493-8731-0.

16 Perucca, F and Pouradier, G (1996). The rubbish on our plates. Prion Books, London. ISBN 1-85375-233-1.

17 Plant, J (2000). Your life in your hands. Understanding, preventing, and overcoming breast cancer. Virgin, London. ISBN 1-85227-809-9.

18 van Alphen, J, Feron, JBR, Frazer, AC, Hoffmann, WG, Hunt, KE, van Stuyvenberg, JH and Tousley, RD (1969). Edited by JH van Stuyvenberg. Margarine - an economic, social, and scientific history, 1869-1969. Liverpool University Press, Liverpool. ISBN 0-85323-130-3.

19 Williams, RJ (1956) Biochemical individuality. The key to understanding what shapes your health. Wiley, New York. [Reprinted 1988 by Keats Publishing, Connecticut.]

20 Wing, HH (1908). Milk and its products. A treatise upon the nature and qualities of dairy milk and the manufacture of butter and cheese. Macmillan, London.

21 Zukin. J (1998). Dairy-free Cookbook. Over 250 recipes for people with lactose intolerance or milk allergy. Prima Health, California. ISBN 0-7615-1467-8.

❖   ❖   ❖

Scientific papers

Historical

1 Cook GC and Kajubi SK (1996). Tribal incidence of lactase deficiency in Uganda. Lancet 1:725-730.

2 Cuatrecasas P, Lockwood, DH and Caldwell JR (1965). Lactase deficiency in the adult. A common occurrence. Lancet 1:14-18.

Diagnosis

1 Arola, H (1994). Diagnosis of hypolactasia and lactose malabsorption. Scand J Gasterenterol 202:26-35.

2 Duncan, A and Hill, PG (2001). A UK survey of laboratory-based gastrointestinal investigations. Ann Clin Biochem 35:492-503.

3 Grimbacher B, Peters T and Peter H-H (1997). Lactose-intolerance may induce severe chronic eczema. Int Arch Allergy Immunol 113:516-518.

4 Joseph, F and Rosenberg, AJ (1988). Breath hydrogen testing: diseased versus normal patients. J Pediatr Gasterenterol Nutr 7:787-791.

5 Kuokkanen, M, Enattah, NS, Oksanen, A, Savilahti, E, Orpana, A and Jarvela, I (2003). Transcriptional regulation of the lactase phlorizin-hydrolase gene by polmorphisms with adult-type hypolactasia. Gut 52:647-652.

6   Matthews SB and Campbell AK (2000). When sugar is not so sweet. Lancet 355:1309.

7   Matthews SB, and Campbell AK (2000). Neuromuscular symptoms associated with lactose intolerance. Lancet 356:511.

8   Matthews SB, Waud J, Roberts A and Campbell AK (2004). Systemic lactose intolerance: a new perspective on an old problem. Postgrad Med J 81:167-173.

9   Matthews, SB and Campbell, AK (2004). Lactose intolerance in the young: a new perspective. Welsh Paediatric J 20:56-66.

10 Moore, BJ. (2003). Dairy foods: are they politically correct. Nutr Today 38:82-90.

11 Rosado, JL, Allen, LH and Solomons, NW (1987). Milk consumption, symptom response, and lactose digestion in milk intolerance. J Clin Nutr 45:1457-1460.

12 Rosaldo, JL, Gonzalez, C, Valencia, ME, Lopez, P, Palma, M, Lopez, B, L-M and Baez, M d C (1994). Lactose maldigestion and milk intolerance: a study in rural and urban Mexico using physiological doses of milk. Nutr 124:1052-1059.

13 Srinivasan D and Minutesocha A (1998). When to suspect lactose intolerance. Symptomatic, ethnic, and laboratory clues. Postgrad Med 104:109-123.

14 Suarez FL, Savaiano DA, Levitt MD (1995). A comparison of symptoms after the consumption of milk or lactose-hydrolyzed milk by people with self-reported severe lactose intolerance. New Eng J Med 333:1-4.

15 Suarez FL, Springfiled J, Furne JK, Lohrmann TT, Kerr PS and Levitt MD (1999). Gas production in humans ingesting a soybean flour derived from beans naturally low in oligosaccharides. Am J Clin Nutr 69:135-139.

16 Tolston, LG (2000). Adult-type lactase deficiency. Nutr Today 35:134-138.

Genetics and evolution

1   Buning, C, Ockenga, J, Kruger, S, Jurga, J, Baier, P, Dignass, A, Vogel, A, Strassburg, C, Weltrich, R, Genschel, J, Lochs, H and Schmidt, H (2003). The C/C_{13910} and G/G_{22028} genotypes for adult-type hypolactasia are not associated with inflammatory bowel disease. Scand J Gasteroenterol 38:538-542.

2   Dudd SN and Evershed, RP (1998). Direct demonstration of milk as an element of archeological economies. Science 282:1478-1481.

3   Enattah, et al (2002). Identification of a variant associated with adult-type hypolactasia. Nature Genetics 30:233-237.

4   Fabrizis, LS and Savaiano, DA (1997). Diet, genetics and lactose. Food Technol 51:74-76.

5   Fang, R, Nilda, AS, Olds, CO and Silbey, E (2000). The homeodomain protein Cdx2 regulates lactase gene promoter activity during enterocyte differentiation. Gasteroenterol 118:115-127.

6   Flatz, G. (1987). Genetics of lactose digestion in humans. Adv Hum Genetics 16:1-77.

7   Hollox, EJ, Poulter, M, Zvarik, M, Ferak, V, Krause, A, Jenkins, T, Saha, N, Kozlov, AI and Swallow, DM (2001). Lactase haplotype diversity in the old world. Am J Hum Genetics 68:160-172.

8   Jarvela, I, Enattah, NS, Kokkonen, J, Varilo, T, Savilahti, E and Peltonen, L (1998). Assignment of the locus for congenital lactase deficiency to 2q21 in the vicinity of, but separate from, the Lactase-Phlorizin-Hydrolase gene. Am J Hum Genetics 63:1078-1085.

9   Sahi, T (1994). Genetics and epidemiology of adult-type hypolactasia. Scand J Gastroenterol 29(suppl); 202:7-20.

10 Swallow, DM (2003). Genetics of lactase persistence and lactose intolerance. Ann Rev Genetics 37:197-219.

Darwin's illness

1   Campbell, AK (2003). What Darwin missed. Astrophys Space Sci 285:571-585.

2   Campbell, AK and Matthews, SB (2005). Darwin's illness revealed. Postgrad Med J 81: 248-251.

Mechanisms and the toxin hypothesis

1   Bock, A and Sawers, G (1997). Fermentation. In: *Escherichia coli* and *Salmonella* 2nd Edition, Vol 1, pp 262-282. Editor: Neidhardt FC. ASM Press, Washington DC.

2   Campbell, AK, Matthews, SB and Wann, KT (2004). Lactose causes heart arrhythmia in the water flea *Daphnia pulex*. Comp Biochem Physiol B 139:225-234.

3   Gibson, GR and Roberfroid, MB, Editors (1999). Colonic microbiota, nutrition and health. Kluwer Academic Press, Dordrecht, Boston, London. ISBN 0-4127-9880-8.

4   Guarner, F and Malagelada, J-R (2003). Gut flora in health and disease. Lancet 361:512-519.

5   Llewellyn, DH, Roderick, L, Sheik, N and Campbell, AK (1996). Calcium stress induces calreticulin gene expression. Biochem J 318:400-410.

6   Paschen, W and Doutheil, J (1999). Disturbance of endoplasmic reticulum functions: a key mechanism underlying cell damage. Acta Neurochir Suppl (Wien) 73:1-5.

7   Quaroni, A, Paul, ECA and Nichols, BL (1993). Post-translational regulation of brush-border enzyme expression in intestinal cells. In: Common food intolerances 2: Milk in human nutrition and adult-type hypolactasia. Editors: Aurrichio, S and Semnza, G. Dyn Nutr Res Basel Karge 3:193-198.

8 Sosulski, FW, Elkowicz, L and Reichart, RD (1982). Oligosaccharides in eleven legumes and their classified protein and starch fractions. J Food Sci 47:498-502.

Leaky gut syndrome

1 Gilbère, G (2004). I was poisoned by my body. Lucky Press, Lancaster, Ohio. ISBN 0-967650-9-1.

2 Lipiski, E. (1998). Leaky gut syndrome. Keat Publishing, Los Angeles. ISBN 0-87983-824-8.

Milk, sugars and disease

1 Elwood, P, Pickering, J, Hughes, J, Fehily, A and Ness, A (2003). Milk drinking, ischaemic heart disease and ischaemic stroke. II. Evidence from cohort studies.

2 Elwood, PC. (2001). Milk, coronary disease and mortality. J Epidemiol Community Health 55:375.

3 Gill, HS and Cross, ML (2000). Anticancer properties of bovine milk. Brit J Nutr 84: Suppl 1, S161-S166.

4 Mann, J (2004). Free sugars and human health: sufficient evidence for action? Lancet 363:1068-1070.

5 McEligot, JA, Rock, CL, Sobo, EJ and Flatt, SW (2000). Food avoidance by women at risk for recurrence of breast cancer. J Cancer Ed 15:151-155.

6 Montonen, J, et al. (2005). Dietary patterns and the incidence of type 2 diabetes. Am J Epidemiol 161:219-227.

7 Moss,M and Freed,D (2002). The cow and the coronary: epidemiology, biochemistry and immunology. Int J Cardiol 87:203-216.

8 Park, M, Ross, GW, Petrovich, H, White PR, Masaki, KH, Nelson, JS, Tanner, CM, Curb, CM, Blanchette, PL and Abbott, RD (2005). Consumption of milk and calcium in midlife and future risk of Parkinson disease. Neurol 64:1047-1051.

9 Segall, JJ (2002). Plausibility of dietary lactose as a coronary risk factor. J Nutr Environ Med 12:217-229.

10 Tsuda, H, Sekine, K, Ushida, Y, Kuhara, T, Takasuka, N, Iigo, M, Han, S and Moore, MA (2000). Milk and dairy products in cancer prevention: focus on bovine lactoferrin. Mutation Res 462:227-233.

11 Webb, PM, Bain, CJ, Purdie, DM, Harvery, PWJ and Green, A (1998). Milk consumption, galactose metabolism, and ovarian cancer. Cancer Causes and Control 9:637-644.

further reading

Soya studies

1   Javobsen, BK, Knutsen, SF and Fraser, GE (1998). Does high soy milk intake reduce prostate cancer incidence? The Adentist Health Study (United States).

2   British Nutrition Foundation (2002). Soya and health - a briefing paper.

3   Sirtori, *et al* (1999). Double-blind study of the addition of high protein soya milk *v.* cow's milk to the diet of patients with severe hypercholesterolaemia and resistance to, or intolerance of, statins. Br J Nutr 82:91-96.

Evolution and biodiversity

1   Campbell AK (2003). Save those molecules! Molecular biodiversity and life. J Applied Ecol 40:193-203.

❖   ❖   ❖

If you are intolerant to lactose, you may have as many as ten of the symptoms described below (see **Table 11**), or just one or two. If so, try removing lactose from your diet for 1 month and record your daily health in a diary during this period.

Table 11. A simple guide to the key symptoms that can be caused by lactose intolerance.

Symptom	How common
Gut	
Abdominal pain	Very common
Gut distension	Very common
Gas	Very common
Tummy rumbling (borborygmi)	Very common
Diarrhoea	Common
Constipation	Common, if no diarrhoea
Feeling sick (nausea)	Common
Vomiting	Common
Systemic	
Severe headache and light-headedness	Common
Loss of concentration and short-term memory	Common
Chronic tiredness	Often
Muscle pain	Often
Joint pain, with or without swelling and stiffness	Often
Allergies (skin rash, itchy skin, runny nose, stuffed-up sinus, wheezing)	Sometimes
Sudden fast beating of the heart (palpitations)	Sometimes
Mouth ulcers	Sometimes
Increased frequency of weeing	Rare
Sore throat	Rare

Key
Very common - most people with lactose intolerance suffer from this.
Common - more than ¾ of people with lactose intolerance suffer from this.
Often - more than ½ of people with lactose intolerance suffer from this.
Sometimes - less than ½ of people with lactose intolerance suffer from this.
Rare - less than ¼ of people with lactose intolerance suffer from this.